STECK-VAUGHN

Review

W9-BPO-689

LANGUAGE

Exercises

STECK-VAUGHN
C O M P A N Y
ELEMENTARY • SECONDARY • ADULT • LIBRARY

Acknowledgments

Executive Editor: Diane Sharpe
Supervising Editor: Stephanie Muller
Project Editor: Patricia Claney
Design Manager: Richard Balsam

Macmillan/McGraw-Hill School Publishing Company: Pronunciation Key,
reprinted with permission of the publisher, from *Macmillan School Dictionary 1*.
Copyright © 1990 Macmillan Publishing Company, a division of Macmillan, Inc.

LANGUAGE EXERCISES Series:

Level A	Level D	Level G
Level B	Level E	Level H
Level C	Level F	Review

ISBN 0-8114-6313-3

Table of Contents

Unit 6 Study Skills

Final Reviews

Lesson 1

Synonyms and Antonyms

■ A **synonym** is a word that has the same or nearly the same meaning as
one or more other words.   EXAMPLES: reply – answer   talk – speak

A. Write a synonym for each word below.

1. pleasant _____

2. enough _____

3. leave_____

4. inquire _____

5. fearless_____

6. artificial _____

7. famous _____

8. trade _____

9. house _____

10. nation _____

11. difficult _____

12. vacant _____

**B. Write four sentences about recycling. In each sentence, use a synonym for the word in
parentheses. Underline the synonym.**

1. (packaging) _____

2. (waste) _____

3. (landfill) _____

4. (planet) _____

■ An **antonym** is a word that has the opposite meaning of another word.
EXAMPLES: old – new   bad – good

C. Write an antonym for each word below.

1. failure_____

2. absent _____

3. before _____

4. slow_____

5. all _____

6. forget _____

7. love _____

8. no_____

9. friend _____

10. always _____

11. light_____

12. forward_____

**D. In each sentence, write an antonym for the word in parentheses that makes sense in
the sentence.**

1. Thao ran his hand along the (smooth) _____ surface of the wood.

2. He knew he would have to (stop) _____ sanding it.

3. Only after sanding would he be able to (destroy) _____ a table.

4. He would try to (forget) _____ not to sand it too much.

> ■ A **homonym** is a word that sounds the same as another word but has a different spelling and a different meaning.
> EXAMPLES: their – they're – there   hear – here

A. Underline the correct homonym(s) in each sentence below.

1. What is the (weight, wait) of that rocket?

2. The (sale, sail) on the lake will be rough today.

3. Don't you like to (brows, browse) around in a bookstore?

4. We spent several (days, daze) at an old-fashioned (in, inn).

5. The ship was caught in an ice (flow, floe).

6. A large (boulder, bolder) rolled down the mountainside.

7. Why is that crowd on the (pier, peer)?

8. They asked the bank for a (lone, loan).

9. We drove four miles in a foggy (missed, mist).

10. Don't you like to (sea, see) a field of golden wheat?

11. Jack (threw, through) the ball (threw, through) the garage window.

12. We (buy, by) our fish from the market down on the (beach, beech).

13. The band will march down the middle (aisle, isle) of the auditorium.

14. Who is the (principal, principle) of your school?

15. The United States Congress (meats, meets) in the capitol in Washington, D.C.

16. The farmer caught the horse by the (rain, reign, rein).

17. She stepped on the (break, brake) suddenly.

18. (Their, There) are too many people to get on this boat.

19. The wren (flew, flue) in a (strait, straight) line.

20. We were not (allowed, aloud) to visit the museum yesterday.

B. Write a homonym for each word below.

1. weigh _____

2. steal _____

3. sail _____

4. fare _____

5. maid _____

6. deer _____

7. ate _____

8. vain _____

9. strait _____

10. threw _____

11. soar _____

12. bored _____

13. see _____

14. sent _____

15. pare _____

16. peace _____

17. sun _____

18. blue _____

Lesson 3

Homographs

> ■ A **homograph** is a word that has the same spelling as another word but a different meaning and sometimes a different pronunciation.
>
> EXAMPLE: <u>saw</u>, meaning "have seen," and <u>saw</u>, meaning "a tool used for cutting"

A. Circle the letter for the definition that best defines each underlined homograph.

1. Sara jumped at the <u>bangs</u> of the exploding balloons.

   a. fringe of hair   **b.** loud noises

2. She grabbed a stick to <u>arm</u> herself against the threat.

   a. part of the body   **b.** take up a weapon

3. The dog's <u>bark</u> woke the family.

   a. noise a dog makes   **b.** outside covering on a tree

4. Mix the pancake <u>batter</u> for three minutes.

   a. person at bat   **b.** mixture for cooking

B. Use the homographs in the box to complete the sentences below. Each homograph will be used twice.

1. Pieces of a board game are _____.

   People who are cashiers are _____.

2. A water bird is a _____.

   To lower the head is to _____.

3. A metal container is a _____.

   If you are able, you _____.

4. To get down from something is to _____.

   If something is on fire, it is _____.

duck
alight
can
checkers

C. Write the homograph for each pair of meanings below. The first letter of each word is given for you.

1. **a.** building for horses   **b.** delay   s_____

2. **a.** a metal fastener   **b.** a sound made with fingers   s_____

3. **a.** to crush   **b.** a yellow vegetable   s_____

4. **a.** a bad doctor   **b.** the sound made by a duck   q_____

5. **a.** to strike   **b.** a party fruit drink   p_____

- A **prefix** added to the beginning of a base word changes the meaning of the word.
  EXAMPLE: un-, meaning "not," + the base word <u>done</u> = <u>undone</u>, meaning "not done"
- Some prefixes have one meaning, and others have more than one meaning.

  EXAMPLES:

prefix	meaning
im-, in-, non-, un-	not
dis-, in-, non-	opposite of, lack of, not
mis-	bad, badly, wrong, wrongly
pre-	before
re-	again

A. Add the prefix <u>un-</u>, <u>im-</u>, <u>non-</u>, or <u>mis-</u> to the base word in parentheses. Write the new word in the sentence. Then write the definition of the new word on the line after the sentence. Use a dictionary if necessary.

1. It is _____ (practical) to put a new monkey into a cage with other monkeys.

_____

2. The monkeys might _____ (behave) with a newcomer among them.

_____

3. They will also feel quite _____ (easy) for a number of days or even weeks.

_____

4. Even if the new monkey is _____ (violent) in nature, the others may harm it.

_____

5. Sometimes animal behavior can be quite _____ (usual).

_____

B. Underline each prefix. Write the meaning of each word that has a prefix.

1. unexpected guest _____

2. really disappear _____

3. disagree often _____

4. misspell a name _____

5. preview a movie _____

6. reenter a room _____

7. misplace a shoe _____

8. impossible situation _____

9. nonstop reading _____

10. unimportant discussion _____

11. insane story _____

12. prejudge a person _____

Lesson 5

Suffixes

- A **suffix** added to the end of a base word changes the meaning of the word.
  EXAMPLE: -ful, meaning "full of," + the base word <u>joy</u> = <u>joyful</u>,
  meaning "full of joy"
- Some suffixes have one meaning, and others have more than one meaning.
  EXAMPLES:

suffix	meaning
-able	able to be, suitable or inclined to
-al	relating to, like
-ful	as much as will fill, full of
-less	without, that does not
-ous	full of
-y	having, full of

A. Add a suffix from the list above to the base word in parentheses. Write the new word. Then write the definition of the new word on the line after the sentence. Do not use any suffix more than once.

1. Switzerland is a _____ country.   (mountain)

   _____

2. If you visit there, it is _____ to have a walking stick.   (help)

   _____

3. Many tourists visit the country's _____ mountains to ski each year.   (snow)

   _____

4. The Swiss people have a great deal of _____ pride.   (nation)

   _____

5. Many Swiss are _____ about several languages.   (knowledge)

   _____

B. Underline each suffix. Write the meaning of each word that has a suffix.

1. breakable toy _____

2. endless waves _____

3. hazardous path _____

4. inflatable raft _____

5. poisonous snake _____

6. dependable trains _____

7. humorous program _____

8. tearful goodbye _____

9. bumpy ride _____

10. careless driver _____

11. natural food _____

12. magical wand _____

Contractions

- A **contraction** is a word formed by joining two other words.
- An **apostrophe** shows where a letter or letters have been left out.   EXAMPLE: do not = don't
- Won't is an exception.   EXAMPLE: will not = won't

A. Underline each contraction. Write the words that make up each contraction on the line.

1. Stingrays look as if they're part bird, part fish. _____

2. Stingrays cover themselves with sand so they won't be seen. _____

3. There's a chance that waders might step on a stingray and get stung. _____

4. That's a painful way to learn that you shouldn't forget about stingrays.

   _____   _____

5. Until recently, stingrays weren't seen very often. _____

6. It doesn't seem likely, but some stingrays will eat out of divers' hands. _____

7. Because its mouth is underneath, the stingray can't see what it's eating.

   _____   _____

8. Once they've been fed by hand, they'll flutter around for more.

   _____   _____

9. It's hard to believe these stingrays aren't afraid of humans.

   _____   _____

10. To pet a stingray, they'd gently touch its velvety skin. _____

B. Find the pairs of words that can be made into contractions. Underline each pair. Then write the contraction each word pair can make on the lines following the sentences.

1. I have never tried scuba diving, but I would like to.

   _____   _____

2. It is a good way to explore what is under the water.

   _____   _____

3. First, I will need to take lessons in the pool. _____

4. Then I can find out what to do if the equipment does not work. _____

Compound Words

■ A **compound word** is a word that is made up of two or more words. The meaning of many compound words is related to the meaning of each individual word.

> EXAMPLE: blue + berry = blueberry, meaning "a type of berry that is blue in color"

■ Compound words may be written as one word, as hyphenated words, or as two separate words. Always check a dictionary.

A. Combine the words in the list to make compound words. You may use words more than once.

air	knob	door	port	paper	condition	black	berry
sand	line	stand	under	way	ground	bird	sea

1. _____

2. _____

3. _____

4. _____

5. _____

6. _____

7. _____

8. _____

9. _____

10. _____

11. _____

12. _____

B. Answer the following questions.

1. Whirl means "to move in circles." What is a whirlpool?

_____

2. Since quick means "moves rapidly," what is quicksand?

_____

3. Rattle means "to make sharp, short sounds quickly." What is a rattlesnake?

_____

4. A ring is "a small, circular band." What is an earring?

_____

5. Pool can mean "a group of people who do something together." What is a car pool?

_____

6. A lace can be "a string or cord that is used to hold something together." What is a shoelace?

_____

Connotation/Denotation

> - The **denotation** of a word is its exact meaning as stated in a dictionary.
>   EXAMPLE: The denotation of casual is "not fancy or formal."
> - The **connotation** of a word is an added meaning that suggests something positive or negative.
>   EXAMPLES: **Negative:** Sloppy suggests "very messy." Sloppy has a negative connotation.
>   **Positive:** Casual suggests "informal or relaxed." Casual has a positive connotation.
> - Some words are neutral. They do not suggest either good or bad feelings.
>   EXAMPLES: calendar, toy, pencil

A. Write (−) if the word has a negative connotation. Write (+) if it has a positive connotation. Write (N) if the word is neutral.

1. _____ lazy
   _____ relaxed

2. _____ determined
   _____ stubborn

3. _____ drug
   _____ remedy

4. _____ clever
   _____ sneaky

5. _____ pretty
   _____ gorgeous

6. _____ grand
   _____ large

7. _____ old
   _____ antique

8. _____ curious
   _____ nosy

9. _____ make
   _____ create

10. _____ weird
    _____ unique

11. _____ criticize
    _____ evaluate

12. _____ snooty
    _____ refined

B. Rewrite the paragraph below. Replace the underlined words with words that do not have a negative connotation.

Jason shoved his way through the mob of people. He swaggered through the doorway and slouched against the wall. His clothes were quite gaudy. He glared at everyone with hostile eyes. Then he snickered and said in a loud tone, "I'm finally here."

_____

_____

_____

_____

_____

_____

_____

Idioms

> ■ An **idiom** is an expression that has a meaning different from the usual
> meanings of the individual words within it.
>   EXAMPLE: We're all in the same boat means "We're in a similar situation,"
>   not, "We're all in a watercraft together."

**A. Read each sentence. Then write the letter of the corresponding idiom for the
underlined word or words.**

A. shaken up	**D.** beside herself	**G.** comes through	**J.** down in the dumps
B. fly off the handle	**E.** in a bind	**H.** in the doghouse	**K.** stands up for
C. on cloud nine	**F.** put up with	**I.** on the fence	

1. One day Julia will be <u>sad</u>. _____

2. The next day you may find her <u>unbelievably happy</u>. _____

3. But be careful when Julia is <u>very scared or confused</u>. _____

4. She's liable to <u>become suddenly angry</u>. _____

5. Julia always <u>defends</u> her views, no matter what. _____

6. She won't <u>allow</u> any argument. _____

7. One time when I insisted that she listen to my viewpoint, she was <u>really upset</u>. _____

8. I was <u>out of favor</u> for weeks. _____

9. On the other hand, when a friend of Julia's is <u>in a difficult situation</u>, she really <u>helps</u>. _____ _____

10. Like a true friend, Julia is there when I am <u>unable to make a decision</u>. _____

**B. For the underlined idiom in each sentence below, write the usual meaning of the
words that make up the idiom.**

1. Kelly can't decide whether she wants to go, so our plans are still <u>up in the air</u>. _____undecided_____

2. If I get the job, I'll be <u>walking on air</u>. _____

3. My friend's business is <u>on the skids</u>. _____

4. George's ideas are <u>off the wall</u>. _____

5. That's enough silliness. Let's <u>talk turkey</u>. _____

6. Victor was <u>in hot water</u> for not cleaning the garage. _____

7. The audience was <u>all ears</u> when you spoke. _____

8. The lost book <u>turned up</u> yesterday. _____

9. Jan and I <u>put our heads together</u> to solve the problem. _____

A. Write S before each pair of synonyms. Write A before each pair of antonyms.

_____ **1.** quiet, noisy   _____ **5.** healthy, sick   _____ **9.** fast, quick

_____ **2.** fearless, brave   _____ **6.** calm, peaceful   _____ **10.** cry, weep

_____ **3.** begin, start   _____ **7.** lost, found   _____ **11.** bottom, top

_____ **4.** gentle, rough   _____ **8.** night, day   _____ **12.** dull, sharp

B. Using the homonyms in parentheses, write the correct words on the lines.

1. (week, weak)   Anna was _____ for a _____ after she had the flu.

2. (right, write)   Did you _____ down the _____ address?

3. (blew, blue)   The wind _____ leaves and twigs into the beautiful _____ water.

4. (read, red)   Meg _____ a poem about a young girl with _____ hair and freckles.

5. (pane, pain)   Maria felt a _____ in her hand when she tried to remove the broken

window _____ .

C. Circle the letter of the best definition for each underlined homograph.

1. John <u>flies</u> to California every summer to visit his family.

   a. insects   **b.** moves in the air

2. Mr. Bailey owns a fruit and vegetable <u>stand</u>.

   a. to be on one's feet   **b.** a small, open structure

3. The band enjoyed performing at the <u>ball</u>.

   a. a large formal dance   **b.** a round body or object

4. Don't forget to <u>wind</u> the alarm clock before you go to bed.

   a. air movement   **b.** to tighten a spring

D. Choose an appropriate prefix or suffix from the box for each of the underlined words below. Write the new word on the line.

| dis-   mis-   re-   un-   -ish   -ful   -less   -en |

1. full of <u>thanks</u> _____   **5.** to make <u>black</u> in color _____

2. to <u>pay</u> again _____   **6.** without <u>thanks</u> _____

3. to not <u>agree</u> _____   **7.** not <u>happy</u> _____

4. act as a <u>fool</u> _____   **8.** <u>take</u> wrongly _____

E. Underline the pair of words that can be written as a contraction in each sentence. Then write each contraction on the line.

_____ **1.** Yolanda does not want to work late today.

_____ **2.** She would rather come in early tomorrow.

_____ **3.** It is getting dark.

_____ **4.** She does not like driving in the dark.

_____ **5.** You must not blame her.

_____ **6.** Who is going to stay with her?

_____ **7.** James did not volunteer.

F. Combine two words in each sentence to make a compound word. Write the word on the line.

1. I polished the brass knob on the door. _____

2. Lynn rested her swollen foot on the stool. _____

3. The police tried to block the road to catch the thief. _____

4. Please walk on the left side of the street. _____

5. I keep my green plants in my warm house during the winter. _____

G. Write (–) if the underlined word has a negative connotation. Write (+) if the underlined word has a positive connotation.

_____ **1.** Joe is sometimes narrow-minded.

_____ **2.** Marie is very outgoing.

_____ **3.** Do you like to gossip?

_____ **4.** Carla can gab for hours.

_____ **5.** Let's donate this later.

_____ **6.** The child grabbed the toy and ran away.

_____ **7.** Those insects are real pests.

_____ **8.** I demand that you listen to me.

_____ **9.** The mansion was very old.

_____ **10.** Steve drives an old jalopy.

H. Underline the idiom in each sentence. Then write what the idiom means.

1. Since there was little time, the mayor only hit the high spots of his speech.

_____

2. The committee's bank account was low, so they had to cut corners on their party.

_____

3. Mark couldn't find a job, so he asked his uncle to pull some strings for him.

_____

A. Rewrite the following sentences, using synonyms for the underlined words.

1. The lightning flashed across the <u>black</u> sky as the trees <u>bent</u> in the wind.

   _____

2. <u>Blasts</u> of wind whistled through the <u>openings</u> between the boards on the window.

   _____

3. Then a <u>hush</u> seemed to fall over our part of the <u>world</u>.

   _____

B. Rewrite the following sentences, using antonyms for the underlined words.

1. <u>Before</u> the storm hit, the sky got <u>darker</u>.

   _____

2. <u>Black</u> clouds drifted across the <u>evening</u> sky.

   _____

3. The <u>heavy</u> wind was blowing leaves <u>over</u> the trees.

   _____

C. Write a sentence using a homonym for each word.

1. new _____

2. grater _____

3. choose _____

4. weight _____

5. waist _____

D. For each homograph below, write two sentences. Be sure to use a different meaning of the homograph in each sentence.

1. light   a. _____

      b. _____

2. shed   a. _____

      b. _____

3. rest   a. _____

      b. _____

E. Add one of the following prefixes or suffixes to each base word to make a new word.

> **Prefixes:** in-, non-, dis-, mis-, pre-, re-
> **Suffixes:** -able, -ful, -less

1. place _____
2. direct _____
3. use _____
4. measure _____
5. speech _____

6. tire _____
7. remark _____
8. spell _____
9. pay _____
10. fund _____

F. Use the following idioms in sentences. Use a dictionary if necessary.

1. throw in the towel _____
2. pulling my leg _____
3. skating on thin ice _____
4. get in touch with _____
5. keep an eye on _____

G. Think of words that have almost the same meaning as the neutral word, but have a more negative or positive connotation. Complete the chart with your words.

Negative Connotation	Neutral	Positive Connotation
1. _____	wet	_____
2. _____	shout	_____
3. _____	thin	_____
4. _____	old	_____
5. _____	talk	_____
6. _____	clothes	_____
7. _____	ask	_____
8. _____	work	_____
9. _____	cut	_____
10. _____	eat	_____

■ A **sentence** is a group of words that expresses a complete thought.
EXAMPLE: Marie sings well.

■ **Some of the following groups of words are sentences, and some are not. Write S̲ before each group that is a sentence. Punctuate each sentence with a period.**

_____ **1.** When the downhill skiing season begins___

_____ **2.** Last summer I visited my friend in New Jersey___

_____ **3.** From the very beginning of the first-aid lessons___

_____ **4.** One of the children from the neighborhood___

_____ **5.** A visiting musician played the organ___

_____ **6.** On the way to school this morning___

_____ **7.** "I love you, Mother," said Mike___

_____ **8.** The blue house at the corner of Maple Street___

_____ **9.** After Emily left, the phone rang off the hook___

_____ **10.** Speak distinctly and loudly so that you can be heard___

_____ **11.** I have finally learned to drive our car___

_____ **12.** This is William's tenth birthday___

_____ **13.** At the very last moment, we were ready___

_____ **14.** When you speak in front of people___

_____ **15.** The basket of fruit on the table___

_____ **16.** Please answer the telephone, Julia___

_____ **17.** Hurrying to class because he is late___

_____ **18.** The first thing in the morning___

_____ **19.** That mistake was costly and unfortunate___

_____ **20.** We are planning to build a new doghouse___

_____ **21.** The dog chased the cat up the tree___

_____ **22.** Daniel Boone was born in Pennsylvania___

_____ **23.** The giant cottonwood in our backyard___

_____ **24.** Marla, bring my notebook___

_____ **25.** On a stool beside the back door___

_____ **26.** Sometimes the noise from the street___

_____ **27.** Somewhere out of state___

_____ **28.** The band played a lively march___

_____ **29.** That flight arrived on time___

_____ **30.** Was cracked in dozens of places___

Lesson 11

Types of Sentences

> - A **declarative sentence** makes a statement. It is followed by a period (.).   EXAMPLE: Alicia is my cousin.
> - An **interrogative sentence** asks a question. It is followed by a question mark (?).   EXAMPLE: Where are you going?
> - An **imperative sentence** expresses a command or request. It is followed by a period (.).   EXAMPLE: Close the door.
> - An **exclamatory sentence** expresses strong emotion. It can also express a command or request that is made with great excitement. It is followed by an exclamation mark (!).   EXAMPLES: How you frightened me! Look at that accident!

- Write **D** for declarative, **IN** for interrogative, **IM** for imperative, or **E** for exclamatory before each sentence. Put the correct punctuation at the end of each sentence.

_____ **1.** Everyone will be here by nine o'clock____

_____ **2.** Train your mind to do its work efficiently____

_____ **3.** How does a canal lock work____

_____ **4.** Prepare each day's assignment on time____

_____ **5.** Are we going to the game now____

_____ **6.** Who brought these delicious peaches____

_____ **7.** Our guests have arrived____

_____ **8.** What is meant by rotation of crops____

_____ **9.** Please bring a glass of water____

_____ **10.** Stop that noise____

_____ **11.** Always stand erect____

_____ **12.** Who arranged these flowers____

_____ **13.** Anna, what do you have in that box____

_____ **14.** The Vikings were famous sailors____

_____ **15.** Have you solved all the problems in our lesson____

_____ **16.** Jack, hand me that wrench____

_____ **17.** What is the capital of California____

_____ **18.** Cultivate a pleasant manner____

_____ **19.** How is a pizza made____

_____ **20.** Block that kick____

_____ **21.** A nation is measured by the character of its people____

_____ **22.** Are you an early riser____

_____ **23.** Practice good table manners____

> - Every sentence has two main parts, a **complete subject** and a **complete predicate**.
> - The complete subject includes all the words that tell who or what the sentence is about.
>   EXAMPLES: **My brother**/likes to go with us. **Six geese**/honked loudly.
> - The complete predicate includes all the words that state the action or condition of the subject.
>   EXAMPLES: My brother/**likes to go with us**. Six geese/**honked loudly**.

A. Draw a line between the complete subject and the complete predicate in each sentence.

1. Bees/fly.

2. Trains whistle.

3. A talented artist drew this cartoon.

4. The wind blew furiously.

5. My grandmother made this dress last year.

6. We surely have enjoyed the holiday.

7. These cookies are made with rice.

8. This letter came to the post office box.

9. They rent a cabin in Colorado every summer.

10. Jennifer is reading about the pioneer days in the West.

11. Our baseball team won the third game of the series.

12. The band played a cheerful tune.

13. A cloudless sky is a great help to a pilot.

14. The voice of the auctioneer was heard throughout the hall.

15. A sudden flash of lightning startled us.

16. The wind howled down the chimney.

17. Paul's dog followed him to the grocery store.

18. Their apartment is on the sixth floor.

19. We have studied many interesting places.

20. Each player on the team deserves credit for the victory.

21. Forest rangers fought the raging fire.

22. A friend taught Robert a valuable lesson.

23. Millions of stars make up the Milky Way.

24. The airplane was lost in the thick clouds.

25. Many of the children waded in the pool.

26. Yellowstone Park is a large national park.

27. Cold weather is predicted for tomorrow.

28. The trees were covered with moss.

B. Write a sentence by adding a complete predicate to each complete subject.

1. All of the students _____

2. Elephants _____

3. The top of the mountain _____

4. The television programs tonight _____

5. I _____

6. Each of the girls _____

7. My father's truck _____

8. The dam across the river _____

9. Our new station wagon _____

10. You _____

11. The books in our bookcase _____

12. The mountains _____

13. Today's paper _____

14. The magazine staff _____

C. Write a sentence by adding a complete subject to each complete predicate.

1. _____ is the largest city in Mexico.

2. _____ came to our program.

3. _____ is a valuable mineral.

4. _____ grow beside the road.

5. _____ traveled day and night.

6. _____ was a great inventor.

7. _____ wrote the letter of complaint.

8. _____ met us at the airport.

9. _____ made ice cream for the picnic.

10. _____ made a nest in our tree.

11. _____ lives near the shopping center.

12. _____ have a meeting on Saturday.

Simple Subjects and Predicates

- The **simple subject** of a sentence is the main word in the complete subject. The simple subject is a noun or a word that stands for a noun.
    EXAMPLE: My **sister**/lost her gloves.
- Sometimes the simple subject is also the complete subject.
    EXAMPLE: **She**/lost her gloves.
- The **simple predicate** of a sentence is a verb within the complete predicate. The simple predicate may be a one-word verb or a verb of more than one word.
    EXAMPLES: She/**lost** her gloves. She/**is looking** for them.

- **Draw a line between the complete subject and complete predicate in each sentence below. Underline the simple subject once and the simple predicate twice.**

1. A sudden <u>clap</u> of thunder/<u>frightened</u> all of us.

2. The soft snow covered the fields and roads.

3. We drove very slowly over the narrow bridge.

4. The students are making an aquarium.

5. Our class read about the founder of Hull House.

6. The women were talking in the park.

7. This album has many folk songs.

8. We are furnishing the sandwiches for tonight's picnic.

9. All the trees on that lawn are giant oaks.

10. Many Americans are working in foreign countries.

11. The manager read the names of the contest winners.

12. Bill brought these large melons.

13. We opened the front door of the house.

14. The two mechanics worked on the car for an hour.

15. Black and yellow butterflies fluttered among the flowers.

16. The child spoke politely.

17. We found many beautiful shells along the shore.

18. The best part of the program is the dance number.

19. Every ambitious person is working hard.

20. Sheryl swam across the lake two times.

21. Our program will begin promptly at eight o'clock.

22. The handle of this basket is broken.

23. The clock in the tower strikes every hour.

24. The white farmhouse on that road belongs to my cousin.

25. The first game of the season will be played tomorrow.

- When the subject of a sentence comes before the verb, the sentence is in **natural order.**   EXAMPLE: Henry went to the park.
- When the verb or part of the verb comes before the subject, the sentence is in **inverted order.**   EXAMPLES: Here are the calculators. Down came the rain.
- Many questions are in inverted order.   EXAMPLE: Where is the restaurant?
- Sometimes the subject of a sentence is not expressed, as in a command or request. The understood subject is you.   EXAMPLES: Call about the job now. (You) call about the job now.

- **Rewrite each inverted sentence in natural order. Underline the simple subject once and the simple predicate twice. Add you as the subject to commands or requests.**

1. When is the movie playing?

   _____

2. Never will I forget my first train trip.

   _____

3. Here is the picture I want to buy.

   _____

4. Seldom has he been ill.

   _____

5. Out went the lights.

   _____

6. There were bookcases on all sides of the room.

   _____

7. Take the roast from the oven.

   _____

8. Around the sharp curve swerved the speeding car.

   _____

9. Get out of the swimming pool.

   _____

10. Study for the spelling test.

    _____

11. There are two children in the pool.

    _____

Compound Subjects

> ■ A **compound subject** is made up of two or more simple subjects.
> EXAMPLE: **Henri** and **Tanya** / are tall people.

A. Draw a line between the complete subject and the complete predicate in each sentence. Write <u>SS</u> for a simple subject. Write <u>CS</u> for a compound subject.

<u>CS</u>   **1.** Arturo and I / often work late on Friday.

_____ **2.** Sandy left the person near the crowded exit.

_____ **3.** She and I will mail the packages to San Francisco, California, today.

_____ **4.** Shanghai and New Delhi are two cities visited by the group.

_____ **5.** The fire spread rapidly to other buildings in the neighborhood.

_____ **6.** Luis and Lenora helped their parents with the chores.

_____ **7.** Swimming, jogging, and hiking were our favorite sports.

_____ **8.** Melbourne and Sydney are important Australian cities.

_____ **9.** Eric and I had an interesting experience Saturday.

_____ **10.** The Red Sea and the Mediterranean Sea are connected by the Suez Canal.

_____ **11.** The Republicans and the Democrats made many speeches before the election.

_____ **12.** The people waved to us from the top of the cliff.

_____ **13.** Liz and Jim crated the freshly-picked apples.

_____ **14.** Clean clothes and a neat appearance are important in an interview.

_____ **15.** The kitten and the old dog are good friends.

_____ **16.** David and Paul are on their way to the swimming pool.

_____ **17.** Tom combed his dog's shiny black coat.

_____ **18.** Redbud and dogwood trees bloom in the spring.

_____ **19.** I hummed a cheerful tune on the way to the meeting.

_____ **20.** Buffalo, deer, and antelope once roamed the plains of North America.

_____ **21.** Gina and Hiroshi raked the leaves.

_____ **22.** Brasília and São Paulo are two cities in Brazil.

_____ **23.** Hang gliding is a popular sport in Hawaii.

_____ **24.** Our class went on a field trip to the aquarium.

_____ **25.** The doctor asked him to get a blood test.

B. Write two sentences containing compound subjects.

1. _____

2. _____

Compound Predicates

■ A **compound predicate** is made up of two or more simple predicates.
   EXAMPLE: Joseph / **dances** and **sings.**

A. Draw a line between the complete subject and the complete predicate in each sentence. Write <u>SP</u> for each simple predicate. Write <u>CP</u> for each compound predicate.

<u> CP </u> **1.** Edward / grinned and nodded.

_____ **2.** Plants need air to live.

_____ **3.** Old silver tea kettles were among their possessions.

_____ **4.** My sister buys and sells real estate.

_____ **5.** Snow covered every highway in the area.

_____ **6.** Mr. Sanders designs and makes odd pieces of furniture.

_____ **7.** Popcorn is one of my favorite snack foods.

_____ **8.** Soccer is one of my favorite sports.

_____ **9.** The ducks quickly crossed the road and found the ducklings.

_____ **10.** They came early and stayed late.

_____ **11.** Crystal participated in the Special Olympics this year.

_____ **12.** José raked and sacked the leaves.

_____ **13.** Perry built the fire and cooked supper.

_____ **14.** We collected old newspapers for the recycling center.

_____ **15.** Doug arrived in Toronto, Ontario, during the afternoon.

_____ **16.** Tony's parents are visiting in Oregon and Washington.

_____ **17.** The Garzas live in that apartment building on Oak Street.

_____ **18.** The shingles were picked up and delivered today.

_____ **19.** The audience talked and laughed before the performance.

_____ **20.** Automobiles crowd and jam that highway early in the morning.

_____ **21.** The apples are rotting in the boxes.

_____ **22.** The leader of the group grumbled and scolded.

_____ **23.** She worked hard and waited patiently.

_____ **24.** Nelson Mandela is a great civil rights activist.

_____ **25.** The supervisor has completed the work for the week.

B. Write two sentences containing compound predicates.

1. _____

2. _____

Lesson 17 Combining Sentences

> - Two sentences in which the subjects are different and the predicates are the same can be combined into one sentence. The two subjects are joined by <u>and</u>.   EXAMPLE: **Hurricanes** are storms. **Tornadoes** are storms. **Hurricanes and tornadoes** are storms.
> - Two sentences in which the subjects are the same and the predicates are different can be combined into one sentence. The two predicates may be joined by <u>or</u>, <u>and</u>, or <u>but</u>.   EXAMPLE: Hurricanes **begin over tropical oceans**. Hurricanes **move inland**. Hurricanes **begin over tropical oceans and move inland.**

■ **Combine each pair of sentences below. Underline the compound subject or the compound predicate in each sentence that you write.**

1. Lightning is part of a thunderstorm. Thunder is part of a thunderstorm.

   _____

2. Thunderstorms usually happen in the spring. Thunderstorms bring heavy rains.

   _____

3. Depending on how close or far away it is, thunder sounds like a sharp crack. Depending on how close or far away it is, thunder rumbles.

   _____

4. Lightning is very exciting to watch. Lightning can be very dangerous.

   _____

5. Lightning causes many fires. Lightning harms many people.

   _____

6. An open field is an unsafe place to be during a thunderstorm. A golf course is an unsafe place to be during a thunderstorm.

   _____

7. Benjamin Franklin wanted to protect people from lightning. Benjamin Franklin invented the lightning rod.

   _____

8. A lightning rod is a metal rod placed on the top of a building. A lightning rod is connected to the ground by a cable.

   _____

   _____

> ■ The **direct object** tells who or what receives the action of the verb. The direct object is a noun or pronoun that follows an action verb.
>
> EXAMPLE: Those countries export **coffee.**
> $\overset{\text{DO}}{}$

■ **Underline the verb in each sentence. Then write <u>DO</u> above each direct object.**

1. Juanita's good driving prevented an accident.

2. Every person should have an appreciation of music.

3. Gene, pass the potatoes, please.

4. Do not waste your time on this project.

5. James, did you keep those coupons?

6. Geraldo collects foreign stamps.

7. Eli Whitney invented the cotton gin.

8. Answer my question.

9. We are picking trophies for our bowling league.

10. Who invented the steamboat?

11. I am reading Hemingway's *The Old Man and the Sea*.

12. The North Star guides sailors.

13. The Phoenicians gave the alphabet to civilization.

14. Every person should study world history.

15. Who made this cake?

16. Can you find a direct object in this sentence?

17. Who wrote the story of Johnny Tremain?

18. We bought several curios for our friends.

19. Tamara read the minutes of our last club meeting.

20. Did you ever make a time budget of your own?

21. Mountains have often affected the history of a nation.

22. Emma and Joe baked a pie.

Indirect Objects

> - The **indirect object** is the noun or pronoun that tells to whom or for whom an action is done. In order to have an indirect object, a sentence must have a direct object.
> - The indirect object is usually placed between the action verb and the direct object.
>
>   IO   DO
> EXAMPLE: Who sold **you** that fantastic **bike?**

- **Underline the verb in each sentence. Then write DO above the direct object and IO above the indirect object.**

                            IO   DO
  1. Certain marine plants <u>give</u> the Red Sea its color.

  2. I gave the cashier a check for twenty dollars.

  3. The magician showed the audience a few of her tricks.

  4. The coach taught them the rules of the game.

  5. Roberto brought us some foreign coins.

  6. This interesting book will give every reader pleasure.

  7. Have you written your brother a letter?

  8. They made us some sandwiches to take on our hike.

  9. The astronaut gave Mission Control the data.

  10. I bought my friend an etching at the art exhibit.

  11. James, did you sell Mike your car?

  12. We have given the dog a thorough scrubbing.

  13. Give the usher your ticket.

  14. Carl brought my brother a gold ring from Mexico.

  15. Hand me a pencil, please.

  16. The conductor gave the orchestra a short break.

  17. Show me the picture of your boat.

  18. I have given you my money.

  19. Give Lee this message.

  20. The club gave the town a new statue.

> ■ A **clause** is a group of words that contains a subject and a predicate. There are two kinds of clauses: **independent clauses** and **subordinate clauses.**
> ■ An **independent clause** can stand alone as a sentence because it expresses a complete thought.
> EXAMPLE: **The students came in** when the bell rang. **The students came in.**

A. Underline the independent clause in each sentence below.

1. Frank will be busy because he is studying.

2. I have only one hour that I can spare.

3. The project must be finished when I get back.

4. Gloria volunteered to do the typing that needs to be done.

5. The work is going too slowly for us to finish on time.

6. Before Nathan started to help, I didn't think we could finish.

7. What else should we do before we relax?

8. Since you forgot to give this page to Gloria, you can type it.

9. After she had finished typing, we completed the project.

10. We actually got it finished before the deadline.

> ■ A **subordinate clause** has a subject and predicate but cannot stand alone as a sentence because it does not express a complete thought. A subordinate clause must be combined with an independent clause to make a sentence.
> EXAMPLE: The stamp **that I bought** was already in my collection.

B. Underline the subordinate clause in each sentence below.

1. The people who went shopping found a great sale.

2. Tony's bike, which is a mountain bike, came from that store.

3. Juana was sad when the sale was over.

4. Marianne was excited because she wanted some new things.

5. Thomas didn't find anything since he went late.

6. The mall where we went shopping was new.

7. The people who own the stores are proud of the beautiful setting.

8. The mall, which is miles away, is serviced by the city bus.

9. We ran as fast as we could because the bus was coming.

10. We were panting because we had run fast.

Adjective and Adverb Clauses

> ■ An **adjective clause** is a subordinate clause that modifies a noun or a pronoun. It answers the adjective question Which one? or What kind? It usually modifies the word directly preceding it. Most adjective clauses begin with a **relative pronoun**. A relative pronoun relates an adjective clause to the noun or pronoun that the clause modifies. Who, whom, whose, which, and that are relative pronouns.
>
> EXAMPLE: Always do the work **that is assigned to you.**
> adjective clause
>
> ■ An **adverb clause** is a subordinate clause that modifies a verb, an adjective, or another adverb. It answers the adverb question How? Under what condition? or Why? Words that introduce adverb clauses are called **subordinating conjunctions.** The many subordinating conjunctions include such words as when, after, before, since, although, and because.
>
> EXAMPLE: We left **when the storm clouds gathered.**
> adverb clause

A. Underline the subordinate clause. Then write adjective or adverb on the line.

_____ 1. John Paul Jones was a hero whose bravery won many victories.

_____ 2. The person who reads the most books will get a prize.

_____ 3. He overslept because he hadn't set the alarm.

_____ 4. Give a rousing cheer when our team comes off the field.

_____ 5. The parrot repeats many things that he hears.

_____ 6. The picnic that we planned was canceled.

B. Add a subordinate clause beginning with the word in parentheses to each independent clause below.

1. The package was gone   (when) _____

_____

2. A depot is a place   (where) _____

_____

3. Brad and I cannot go now   (because) _____

_____

4. Tell me the name of the person   (who) _____

_____

Compound and Complex Sentences

> - A **compound sentence** consists of two or more independent clauses. Each independent clause in a compound sentence can stand alone as a separate sentence. The independent clauses are usually joined by <u>and</u>, <u>but</u>, <u>so</u>, <u>or</u>, <u>for</u>, or <u>yet</u> and a comma.
>   EXAMPLE: I like to dance, but Jim likes to sing.
> - Sometimes a **semicolon (;)** is used to join the independent clauses in a compound sentence.
>   EXAMPLE: I like to dance; Jim likes to sing.
> - A **complex sentence** consists of one independent clause and one or more subordinate clauses.
>   EXAMPLE: **When the fire alarm went off,** everyone left the building.
>   subordinate clause

A. Write CP before each compound sentence. Write CX before each complex sentence.

_____ 1. Our team didn't always win, but we always tried to be good sports.

_____ 2. You may stay, but I am going home.

_____ 3. The rangers who serve in Yellowstone Park know every inch of the ground.

_____ 4. That statement may be correct, but it isn't very polite.

_____ 5. We will meet whenever we can.

_____ 6. The pass was thrown perfectly, but Carlos was too well guarded to catch it.

_____ 7. The toga was worn by ancient Roman youths when they reached the age of twelve.

_____ 8. That song, which is often heard on the radio, was written years ago.

_____ 9. They cannot come for dinner, but they will be here later.

_____ 10. My brother likes dogs, but I prefer cats.

_____ 11. The engine is the heart of the submarine, and the periscope is the eye.

_____ 12. I will call you when it arrives.

_____ 13. Those people who camped here were messy.

_____ 14. Edison was only thirty years old when he invented the talking machine.

_____ 15. She crept silently, for she was afraid.

_____ 16. Move the table, but be careful with it.

_____ 17. Bolivia is the only South American country that does not have a port.

_____ 18. How many stars were in the flag that Key saw "by the dawn's early light"?

_____ 19. The octopus gets its name from two Greek words that mean <u>eight</u> and <u>feet</u>.

_____ 20. You may place the order, but we cannot guarantee shipment.

_____ 21. After the sun set, we built a campfire.

_____ 22. We made hamburgers for dinner, and then we toasted marshmallows.

_____ 23. Some people sang songs; others played games.

_____ 24. When it started to rain, everyone took shelter in their tents.

B. Put brackets [ ] around the independent clauses in each compound sentence below. Then underline the simple subject once and the simple predicate twice in each clause.

1. [The streets are filled with cars], but [the sidewalks are empty].
2. Those apples are too sour to eat, but those pears are perfect.
3. She studies hard, but she saves some time to enjoy herself.
4. They lost track of time, so they were late.
5. Eric had not studied, so he failed the test.
6. Yesterday it rained all day, but today the sun is shining.
7. I set the alarm to get up early, but I couldn't get up.
8. They may sing and dance until dawn, but they will be exhausted.
9. My friend moved to Texas, and I will miss her.
10. They arrived at the theater early, but there was still a long line.
11. Lisa took her dog to the veterinarian, but his office was closed.
12. The black cat leaped, but fortunately it didn't catch the bird.
13. I found a baseball in the bushes, and I gave it to my brother.
14. We loaded the cart with groceries, and we went to the checkout.
15. The stadium was showered with lights, but the stands were empty.
16. The small child whimpered, and her mother hugged her.
17. The dark clouds rolled in, and then it began to rain.

C. In each complex sentence below, underline the subordinate clause.

1. The hummingbird is the only bird that can fly backward.
2. The cat that is sitting in the window is mine.
3. The car that is parked outside is new.
4. Jack, who is a football star, is class president.
5. Bonnie, who is an artist, is also studying computer science.
6. John likes food that is cooked in the microwave.
7. The composer who wrote the music comes from Germany.
8. We missed seeing him because we were late.
9. When Jake arrives, we will tell him what happened.
10. She walked slowly because she had hurt her leg.
11. When she walked to the podium, everyone applauded.
12. If animals could talk, they might have a lot to tell.
13. Many roads that were built in our city are no longer traveled.
14. My address book, which is bright red, is gone.
15. Ann, who is from Georgia, just started working here today.
16. The crowd cheered when the player came to bat.
17. When he hit the ball, everyone cheered.

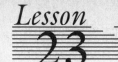

Lesson 23

Correcting Run-on Sentences

> - Two or more independent clauses that are run together without the correct punctuation are called a **run-on sentence.**
>   EXAMPLE: The music was deafening I turned down the volume.
> - One way to correct a run-on sentence is to separate it into two sentences.
>   EXAMPLE: The music was deafening. I turned down the volume.
> - Another way to correct a run-on sentence is to make it into a compound sentence.
>   EXAMPLE: The music was deafening, so I turned down the volume.
> - Another way to correct a run-on sentence is to use a semicolon.
>   EXAMPLE: The music was deafening; I turned down the volume.

- **Correct each run-on sentence below by writing it as two sentences or as a compound sentence.**

1. The city council held a meeting a meeting is held every month.

_____

_____

2. The council members are elected by the voters there are two thousand voters in the city.

_____

_____

3. There is one council member from each suburb, the president is elected by the council members.

_____

_____

4. Those who run for office must give speeches, the speeches should be short.

_____

_____

5. The council decides on many activities every activity is voted on.

_____

_____

6. Money is needed for many of the special activities, the council also plans fund-raisers in the city.

_____

_____

7. The annual city picnic is sponsored by the city council the picnic is in May.

_____

_____

Expanding Sentences

> - Sentences can be **expanded** by adding details to make them clearer and more interesting.   EXAMPLE: The dog ran. The **big black** dog ran **barking into the street.**
> - Details added to sentences may answer these questions: When? Where? How? How often? To what degree? What kind? Which? How many?

A. Expand each sentence below by adding details to answer the questions shown in parentheses. Write the expanded sentence on the line.

1. The crew was ready for liftoff.   (Which? When?)

   _____

2. The shuttle was launched.   (What kind? Where?)

   _____

3. The engines roared.   (How many? To what degree?)

   _____

4. The spacecraft shot up.   (How? Where?)

   _____

5. The astronauts studied the control panels.   (How many? Where?)

   _____

B. Decide how each of the following sentences can be expanded. Write your expanded sentence on the line.

1. The singer ran onto the stage.

   _____

2. The fans leaped up and cheered.

   _____

3. She began to sing.

   _____

4. She strummed the guitar.

   _____

5. The loudspeakers blared.

   _____

6. The fans began dancing.

   _____

A. Label each sentence as follows: Write D for declarative, IN for interrogative, IM for imperative, or E for exclamatory. Write X if it is not a sentence. Punctuate each sentence correctly.

_____ 1. Did you forget our appointment____

_____ 2. Be careful____

_____ 3. Rolled up our sleeping bags____

_____ 4. All members will meet in this room____

_____ 5. Help, I'm frightened____

_____ 6. Where are you going____

_____ 7. Oh, look out ____

_____ 8. People from all over the world____

_____ 9. Julie ran two miles____

_____ 10. Place the books here____

B. In each sentence below, underline the words that are identified in parentheses.

1. (complete subject) The lights around the public square went out.

2. (simple subject) Stations are in all parts of our country.

3. (direct object) Carmen collects fans for a hobby.

4. (complete predicate) We drove slowly across the bridge.

5. (simple predicate) We saw an unusual flower.

6. (compound predicate) Taro swims and dives quite well.

7. (compound subject) The cake and bread are kept in the box.

8. (indirect object) The referee gave our team a fifteen-yard penalty.

9. (direct object) A good citizen obeys the laws, but a bad citizen doesn't.

10. (indirect object) Please lend me your raincoat, so I can stay dry.

C. Write CP after each compound sentence and CX after each complex sentence.

1. The food that is needed will be bought. _____

2. Mary will get lettuce, but we may have some. _____

3. Jack, who said he would help, is late. _____

4. We will go, and they will meet us. _____

5. Jack will drive his car after it has been repaired. _____

6. We are going to Spruce Park since it is on a lake. _____

7. There are canoes that can be rented. _____

8. We can row around the lake, or we can go swimming. _____

9. We can decide what we want to do after we eat our picnic lunch. _____

10. Spruce Park is a great place, and we are going to have a wonderful time. _____

D. **Underline the verb in each sentence. Then write <u>DO</u> above the direct object and <u>IO</u> above the indirect object.**

1. The director gave the actors a new script.

2. Jenny showed her friends her vacation slides.

3. Ms. Lopez took her sick neighbor some chicken soup.

4. We handed the cashier our money.

5. Enrique, please give your brother his jacket.

E. **Underline the independent clause, and circle the subordinate clause in each sentence.**

1. The campers got wet when it started raining.

2. The candidates that I voted for in the election won easily.

3. Before the board voted on the issue, it held public hearings.

4. The freeway through town is a road where vehicles often speed.

5. While we waited, the children kept us entertained.

F. **Underline the subordinate clause in each sentence. Write <u>adjective clause</u> or <u>adverb clause</u> on the line after each sentence.**

1. Meteorologists are people who are trained in weather forecasting. _____

2. Before I decided on a college, I did many hours of research. _____

3. The experiment that I designed failed completely. _____

4. Although the furniture was old, it was very comfortable. _____

5. Many people exercise because they want to stay healthy. _____

6. I ate breakfast before I left. _____

G. **Rewrite each sentence in natural order.**

1. Just below the surface lay a large goldfish.

_____

2. Over the roof flew the baseball.

_____

H. **Combine each pair of sentences to form a compound sentence.**

1. Dogs are Erica's favorite animal. Cats are John's favorite animal.

_____

2. The water reflected the sun. We put on our sunglasses.

_____

A. Read the sentences in the box. Then answer the questions below.

> **A.** Did I give you the tickets for the show?
> **B.** This compact disc is fantastic!
> **C.** Be at my house by seven o'clock.
> **D.** You and I can ride downtown together.
> **E.** We can stop and eat before the show.

1. _____ Which sentence has a compound subject?
2. _____ Which sentence has a compound predicate?
3. _____ Which sentence has a direct object?
4. _____ Which sentence has an indirect object?

5. _____ Which sentence is interrogative?
6. _____ Which sentences are declarative?
7. _____ Which sentence is exclamatory?
8. _____ Which sentence is imperative?

9. What is the complete subject of E? _____

10. What is the simple subject of E? _____

11. What is the complete predicate of C? _____

B. Underline the independent clause, and circle the subordinate clause in each complex sentence below.

1. The streamers sagged after we hung them.

2. Mark knows party planning because he has many parties.

3. Everyone who wants to go to the party must bring something.

4. If everyone brings something, the party will be great.

5. Unless I am wrong, the party is tomorrow.

6. As if everything had been done, Jake ran out of the room.

7. The girls who planned the party received roses.

8. I will never forget the day that I fell on my face at a party.

C. Combine each pair of sentences below to form a compound sentence.

1. The team sat in the dugout. The fans sat in the stands.

_____

2. The rain finally stopped. The game continued.

_____

3. It was the bottom of the ninth inning. There were two outs.

_____

4. The batter swung at the pitch. The umpire called, "Strike three!"

_____

D. Rewrite each inverted sentence below in natural order.

1. Reported on a television bulletin was the news of the storm.

   _____

2. Into the hangar taxied the small airplane.

   _____

3. Down the ramp came the tired passengers.

   _____

E. Create complex sentences by adding a subordinate clause or an independent clause to each group of words.

1. She looked sad _____

2. When she thought about what she said _____

3. This was the time _____

4. After she wrote her apology _____

5. When she wrote it _____

6. Before we left the house _____

F. Rewrite the paragraph below, correcting the run-on sentences.

    In space medicine research, new types of miniature equipment for checking how the body functions have been developed on the spacecraft, astronauts' breathing rates, heartbeats, and blood pressure are taken with miniature devices no larger than a pill. These devices detect the information and transmit it to scientists back on Earth they allow the scientists to monitor astronauts' body responses from a long distance and over long periods of time.

_____

_____

_____

_____

_____

G. Read the two sentences below. Then expand each sentence by adding details to make the sentence clearer and more interesting.

1. The acrobats climbed the ladder.

   _____

2. They began their act.

   _____

Lesson 25

Common and Proper Nouns

> ■ There are two main classes of nouns: **common** and **proper nouns**.
> ■ A **common noun** names any one of a class of objects.
>   EXAMPLES: woman, city, tree
> ■ A **proper noun** names a particular person, place, or thing. It begins with a capital letter.
>   EXAMPLES: Ms. Patel, Chicago, Empire State Building

A. Underline each noun. Then write C or P above it to show whether it is a common or proper noun.

     P   C

1. <u>Maria</u> is my <u>sister</u>.

2. Honolulu is the chief city and capital of Hawaii.

3. Rainbow Natural Bridge is hidden away in the wild mountainous part of southern Utah.

4. The Declaration of Independence is often called the birth certificate of the United States.

5. Abraham Lincoln, Edgar Allan Poe, and Frederic Chopin were born in the same year.

B. Write a proper noun suggested by each common noun.

1. country _____

2. book _____

3. governor _____

4. state _____

5. athlete _____

6. school _____

7. actor _____

8. day _____

9. car _____

10. lake _____

11. singer _____

12. holiday _____

13. newspaper _____

14. river _____

C. Write a sentence using each proper noun and the common noun for its class.

1. Mexico <u>Mexico</u> is another <u>country</u> in North America.

2. December _____

3. Alaska _____

4. Thanksgiving Day _____

5. Bill Clinton _____

6. Tuesday _____

> ■ A **concrete noun** names things you can see and touch.
>   EXAMPLES: apple, dog, fork, book, computer
> ■ An **abstract noun** names an idea, quality, action, or feeling.
>   EXAMPLES: bravery, wickedness, goodness
> ■ A **collective noun** names a group of persons or things.
>   EXAMPLES: crowd, congress, public, United States

■ **Classify each common noun as concrete, collective, or abstract.**

1. humor _____

2. kindness _____

3. army _____

4. danger _____

5. committee _____

6. towel _____

7. jury _____

8. audience _____

9. bird _____

10. orchestra _____

11. fear _____

12. family _____

13. happiness _____

14. truck _____

15. team _____

16. honesty _____

17. bracelet _____

18. society _____

19. album _____

20. courage _____

21. faculty _____

22. club _____

23. photograph _____

24. poverty _____

25. class _____

26. swarm _____

27. table _____

28. goodness _____

29. flock _____

30. radio _____

31. mob _____

32. patience _____

33. herd _____

34. banana _____

35. staff _____

36. mercy _____

37. calculator _____

38. coyote _____

39. generosity _____

40. scissors _____

41. sorrow _____

42. independence _____

Lesson 27

Singular and Plural Nouns

The following chart shows how to change **singular nouns** into **plural nouns.**		
Noun	**Plural Form**	**Examples**
Most nouns	Add -s	ship, ships nose, noses
Nouns ending in a consonant and -y	Change the -y to -i, and add -es	sky, skies navy, navies
Nouns ending in -o	Add -s or -es	hero, heroes piano, pianos
Most nouns ending in -f or -fe	Change the -f or -fe to -ves	half, halves
Most nouns ending in -ch, -sh, -s, or -x	Add -es	bench, benches bush, bushes tax, taxes
Many two-word or three-word compound nouns	Add -s to the principle word	son-in-law, sons-in-law
Nouns with the same form in the singular and plural	No change	sheep

A. Fill in the blank with the plural form of the word in parentheses.

1. (brush)   These are plastic _____.

2. (lunch)   That cafe on the corner serves well-balanced _____.

3. (country)   What _____ belong to the United Nations?

4. (bench)   There are many iron _____ in the park.

5. (earring)   These _____ came from Italy.

6. (calf)   How many _____ are in that pen?

7. (piano)   There are three _____ in the warehouse.

8. (fox)   Did you see the _____ at the zoo?

9. (daisy)   We bought Susan a bunch of _____.

10. (potato)   Do you like baked _____?

11. (dish)   Please help wash the _____.

12. (store)   There are three _____ near my house.

B. Write the correct plural form for each singular noun.

1. booklet _____
2. tomato _____
3. truck _____
4. chef _____
5. branch _____
6. toddler _____
7. penny _____
8. potato _____
9. piece _____
10. door _____
11. island _____
12. country _____
13. house _____
14. garage _____
15. fish _____

16. watch _____
17. elf _____
18. desk _____
19. pan _____
20. sheep _____
21. garden _____
22. pony _____
23. solo _____
24. tree _____
25. light _____
26. church _____
27. city _____
28. spoonful _____
29. vacation _____
30. home _____

C. Rewrite the sentences, changing each underlined singular noun to a plural noun.

1. Put the apple and orange in the box.

_____

2. Jan wrote five letter to her friend.

_____

3. Those building each have four elevator.

_____

4. Our family drove many mile to get to the lake.

_____

5. The top of those car were damaged in the storm.

_____

6. My aunt and uncle attended the family reunion.

_____

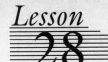

Lesson 28 — Possessive Nouns

> ■ A **possessive noun** shows possession of the noun that follows.
> ■ Form the possessive of most singular nouns by adding an apostrophe (') and -s.
>   EXAMPLES: the boy's hat   Mr. Thomas's car
> ■ Form the possessive of a plural noun ending in -s by adding only an apostrophe.
>   EXAMPLES: the Smiths' home   girls' bikes   sisters' names
> ■ Form the possessive of a plural noun that does not end in -s by adding an apostrophe and -s.
>   EXAMPLES: children's classes   men's books

A. Write the possessive form of each noun.

1. girl _____girl's_____
2. child _____
3. women _____
4. children _____
5. John _____

6. baby _____
7. boys _____
8. teacher _____
9. Dr. Ray _____
10. ladies _____

11. brother _____
12. soldier _____
13. men _____
14. aunt _____
15. Ms. Jones _____

B. Rewrite each phrase using a possessive noun.

1. the cap belonging to Jim   _____Jim's cap_____

2. the wrench that belongs to Kathy   _____

3. the smile of the baby   _____

4. the car that my friend owns   _____

5. the new shoes that belong to Kim _____

6. the collar of the dog   _____

7. the golf clubs that Frank owns   _____

8. the shoes that belong to the runners _____

9. the friends of our parents   _____

10. the opinion of the editor   _____

11. the lunches of the children   _____

12. the coat belonging to Kyle   _____

13. the assignment of the teacher   _____

Lesson

29

Appositives

> ■ An **appositive** is a noun that identifies or explains the noun or pronoun it follows.
>   EXAMPLE: My dog, **Fido,** won a medal.
> ■ An **appositive phrase** consists of an appositive and its modifiers.
>   EXAMPLE: My book, **a novel about the Civil War,** is one of the best I've read.
> ■ Use **commas** to set off an appositive or an appositive phrase that is not essential to the meaning of the sentence.
>   EXAMPLE: John Gray, my uncle, owns that home.
> ■ Don't use commas if the appositive is essential to the meaning of the sentence.
>   EXAMPLES: My brother Kevin arrived late. My other brother Charlie arrived early.

A. Underline the appositive or appositive phrase, and circle the noun that it identifies.

1. Banff, the large Canadian national park, is my favorite place to visit.

2. The painter Vincent Van Gogh cut off part of his ear.

3. The White House, home of the President of the United States, is open to the public for tours.

4. Uncle Marco, my mother's brother, is an engineer.

5. Earth, the only inhabited planet in our solar system, is home to a diverse population of plants and animals.

6. The scorpion, a native of the southwestern part of North America, has a poisonous sting.

7. Emily's prize Persian cat Amelia won first prize at the cat show.

8. Judge Andropov, the presiding judge, sentenced the criminal to prison.

9. Paula's friend from Florida, Luisa, watched a space shuttle launch.

B. Complete each sentence with an appropriate appositive.

1. My friend _____ bought a new bike.

2. The bike, _____, is fast and sleek.

3. Joe and his friend _____ plan to ride their bikes together.

4. They will ride to Pease Park, _____, on Saturday.

5. They plan to meet Anne, _____, on the bike path.

6. After bicycling, they will see a movie, _____.

7. Our friend _____ might come with us.

8. We will get a snack, _____, to eat during the movie.

9. My favorite actor, _____, might be in the movie.

Verbs

- A **verb** is a word that expresses action, being, or state of being.
  EXAMPLES: Leo **traveled** to Europe. Maura **is** an accountant.
- A verb has four principal parts: **present, present participle, past,** and **past participle.**
- For regular verbs, form the present participle by adding -ing to the present. Use a form of the helping verb be with the present participle.
- Form the past and past participle by adding -ed to the present. Use a form of the helping verb have with the past participle.
  EXAMPLES:

Present	Present Participle	Past	Past Participle
listen	(is) listening	listened	(have, had, has) listened
help	(is) helping	helped	(have, had, has) helped
change	(is) changing	changed	(have, had, has) changed

- Irregular verbs form their past and past participle in other ways. A dictionary shows the principal parts of these verbs.

- **Write the present participle, past, and past participle for each verb.**

PRESENT	PRESENT PARTICIPLE	PAST	PAST PARTICIPLE
1. scatter	(is) scattering	scattered	(have, had, has) scattered
2. express			
3. paint			
4. call			
5. cook			
6. observe			
7. look			
8. walk			
9. ramble			
10. shout			
11. notice			
12. order			
13. gaze			
14. borrow			
15. start			
16. work			

Verb Phrases

> ■ Some sentences contain a **verb phrase.** A verb phrase consists of a **main verb** and one or more other verbs.
>
> EXAMPLES: The women **are singing.** Where **have** you **been?**

■ **Underline the verb or verb phrase in each sentence.**

1. The first American schools were held in homes.

2. Who invented the jet engine?

3. *The New England Primer* was the earliest United States textbook.

4. John Philip Sousa was a bandmaster and composer.

5. Who built the first motorcycle?

6. My friends will arrive on Saturday afternoon.

7. What was the final score?

8. Ryan has made this unusual birdhouse.

9. The waves covered the beach with many shells.

10. I have ridden on a motor scooter.

11. The artist is molding clay.

12. Beverly and her friends spent last summer in the mountains.

13. The names of the new employees are posted by the supervisor.

14. Paul has found a new hat.

15. She is going to the store.

16. We have trimmed the hedges.

17. The United States exports many kinds of food.

18. My friend is reading a book about World War I.

19. Jane Addams helped many foreign-born people in Chicago, Illinois.

20. Oil was discovered in many parts of North America.

21. Jenny Lind was called the Swedish Nightingale.

22. We are planning a car trip to Miami, Florida.

23. That dog has howled for two hours.

24. Our guests have arrived.

25. I have written letters to several companies.

26. I can name two important cities in that country.

27. The hummingbird received its name because of the sound of its wings.

28. Jan's poem was printed in the newspaper.

29. Charles and Adam are working at the hamburger stand.

30. This table was painted recently.

> - The **tense** of a verb tells the time of the action or being. There are three simple tenses—present, past, and future.
> - **Present tense** tells about what is happening now.
>   EXAMPLES: Conrad **is** busy. Conrad **studies** hard.
> - **Past tense** tells about something that happened before.
>   EXAMPLE: Conrad **was** sick yesterday.
> - **Future tense** tells about something that will happen. The auxiliary verbs <u>will</u> and <u>shall</u> are used in future tense.
>   EXAMPLES: Conrad **will take** the test tomorrow. I **shall keep** my word.

A. Complete each sentence by writing a verb in the tense shown in parentheses.

1. (future) Hilary _____ tomorrow.

2. (future) Joe _____ her up at the airport.

3. (past) We _____ the house yesterday.

4. (past) Carl _____ reservations for tomorrow night.

5. (present) Hilary _____ my friend.

6. (future) We _____ on a sightseeing tour.

7. (present) I _____ very excited about Hilary's visit.

8. (past) Margaret _____ Toby last week.

B. Write <u>present</u>, <u>past</u>, or <u>future</u> for the tense of each underlined verb.

1. Classes <u>will end</u> next month.   _____

2. We <u>studied</u> hard yesterday.   _____

3. Final exams <u>will start</u> soon.   _____

4. I <u>review</u> every evening.   _____

5. This method <u>worked</u> at midterm.   _____

6. I <u>got</u> A's on my tests then.   _____

7. Marty <u>studies</u> with me.   _____

8. We <u>will study</u> every evening this week.   _____

9. I hardly <u>studied</u> last year.   _____

10. My grades <u>showed</u> it, too.   _____

Present Perfect and Past Perfect Tenses

> - The **perfect tenses** express action that happened before another time or event.
> - The **present perfect** tense tells about something that happened at an indefinite time in the past. The present perfect tense consists of <u>has</u> or <u>have</u> + the past participle.
>   - EXAMPLES: I **have eaten** already. He **has eaten,** too.
> - The **past perfect** tense tells about something that happened before something else in the past. The past perfect tense consists of <u>had</u> + the past participle.
>   - EXAMPLE: I already **had eaten** when they arrived.

A. Write <u>present perfect</u> and <u>past perfect</u> for the tense of the underlined verbs.

_____ 1. Mei <u>had completed</u> high school in June.

_____ 2. She <u>had gone</u> to college in Memphis before coming here.

_____ 3. Mei <u>has decided</u> that she likes her new college.

_____ 4. She <u>had been worried</u> that she wouldn't fit in.

_____ 5. Mei <u>has lived</u> in her house for eight months.

_____ 6. We <u>have tried</u> to make Mei feel welcome.

_____ 7. She <u>has told</u> us a great deal about Memphis.

_____ 8. We <u>had known</u> Memphis was an important city.

_____ 9. However, Mei <u>has described</u> things we never knew!

_____ 10. We <u>have decided</u> that we would like to visit Tennessee some day.

B. Complete each sentence with <u>have</u>, <u>has</u>, or <u>had</u> to form the verb tense indicated in parentheses.

1. (present perfect)   The pitcher _____ left the mound.

2. (present perfect)   The coach and catcher _____ talked to him.

3. (past perfect)   The coach _____ warned him to be careful.

4. (present perfect)   Jason _____ taken his place on the mound.

5. (past perfect)   Jason _____ pitched ten games by the end of last season.

6. (present perfect)   Jason _____ pitched very well.

7. (past perfect)   The team _____ won every game last week.

Using *Is/Are* and *Was/Were*

- Use <u>is</u> with a singular subject.
  EXAMPLE: Tasha **is** the winner.
- Use <u>are</u> with a plural subject.
  EXAMPLE: The boys **are** walking home.
- Always use <u>are</u> with the pronoun <u>you</u>.
  EXAMPLE: You **are** absolutely right!

A. Underline the correct verb to complete each sentence.

1. (Is, Are) this tool ready to be cleaned?

2. They (is, are) making peanut brittle.

3. Bill (is, are) the chairperson this week.

4. Where (is, are) my gloves?

5. This tomato (is, are) too ripe.

6. Ryan, (is, are) these your books?

7. Daniel, (is, are) the sandwiches ready?

8. (Is, Are) you going to sing your solo this morning?

9. This newspaper (is, are) the early edition.

10. Carol asked if you (is, are) still coming to the game.

- Use <u>was</u> with a singular subject to tell about the past.
  EXAMPLE: I **was** there yesterday.
- Use <u>were</u> with a plural subject to tell about the past.
  EXAMPLE: Kevin and Ray **were** not home.
- Always use <u>were</u> with the pronoun <u>you</u>.
  EXAMPLE: You **were** only a few minutes late.

B. Underline the correct verb to complete each sentence.

1. Amy and Crystal (was, were) disappointed because they could not go.

2. Our seats (was, were) near the stage.

3. Taro, Bill, and Luis (was, were) assigned to the first team.

4. These pencils (was, were) made by a company in Chicago.

5. There (was, were) only one carton of milk in the refrigerator.

6. Who (was, were) that person on the corner?

7. She (was, were) at my house this morning.

8. You (was, were) the best swimmer in the contest.

9. Those tomatoes (was, were) delicious!

10. He (was, were) late for work today.

- Never use a helping verb with <u>saw</u>, <u>went</u>, and <u>began</u>.
- Always use a helping verb with <u>seen</u>, <u>gone</u>, and <u>begun</u>.

A. Underline the correct verb.

1. The last person we (saw, seen) in the park was Eric.

2. Who has (went, gone) for the ice?

3. Carla and Yoko (began, begun) to fix the flat tire.

4. Charles (went, gone) to the supermarket for some lettuce.

5. Our summer vacation has (began, begun).

6. They had (saw, seen) a shooting star.

7. Hasn't she (went, gone) to the airport?

8. Yes, we (saw, seen) the concert poster.

9. Alice, have you ever (saw, seen) a penguin?

10. We never (went, gone) to hear the new mayor speak.

11. Olivia, why haven't you (began, begun) your work?

12. Mike (began, begun) to tell us about the accident.

13. Our guests have (went, gone).

14. It (began, begun) to snow early in the evening.

15. Work has finally (began, begun) on the new stadium.

16. We (saw, seen) Pikes Peak last summer.

17. My three sisters (went, gone) to Toronto, Ontario.

18. Have you (saw, seen) the waves pounding the huge boulders?

19. We (went, gone) to hear the symphony last night.

20. They (began, begun) their program with music by Mozart.

21. The program (began, begun) on time.

B. Write a sentence using each verb below.

1. saw _____

2. seen _____

3. gone _____

4. went _____

5. began _____

6. begun _____

- Never use a helping verb with: <u>froze</u> <u>chose</u> <u>spoke</u> <u>broke</u>
- Always use a helping verb with: <u>frozen</u> <u>chosen</u> <u>spoken</u> <u>broken</u>

A. Underline the correct verb form to complete each sentence.

1. Haven't those candidates (spoke, spoken) yet?

2. Has the dessert (froze, frozen) in the molds?

3. I (broke, broken) the handle of the hammer.

4. Have you (spoke, spoken) to your friends about the meeting?

5. Hadn't the coach (chose, chosen) the best players today?

6. The dog has (broke, broken) the toy.

7. Has Anna (spoke, spoken) to you about going with us?

8. We (froze, frozen) the ice for our picnic.

9. I believe you (chose, chosen) the right clothes.

10. Dave, haven't you (broke, broken) your bat?

11. Mr. Mann (spoke, spoken) first.

12. Anthony (froze, frozen) the fruit salad for our picnic.

13. You didn't tell me he had (broke, broken) his arm.

14. The men on the team (chose, chosen) their plays carefully.

15. Ms. Ramirez (spoke, spoken) first.

16. Has the river (froze, frozen) yet?

B. Write the correct past tense form of the verb in parentheses to complete each sentence.

1. (freeze) We could not tell if the ice had _____ overnight.

2. (break) The chain on Ann's bicycle had _____ while she rode.

3. (choose) Carol had _____ to be in the play.

4. (speak) No one _____ while the band played.

5. (choose) Tom has _____ to take both tests today.

6. (choose) Jim _____ not to take the test early.

7. (break) No one knew who had _____ the window.

8. (speak) Carol _____ her lines loudly and clearly.

9. (freeze) It was so cold that everything had _____.

10. (speak) The librarian wanted to know who had _____ so loudly.

Come, Ring, Drink, Know, and Throw

- Never use a helping verb with <u>came</u>, <u>rang</u>, <u>drank</u>, <u>knew</u>, and <u>threw</u>.
- Always use a helping verb with <u>come</u>, <u>rung</u>, <u>drunk</u>, <u>known</u>, and <u>thrown</u>.

A. Underline the correct verb.

1. The tired horse (drank, drunk) from the cool stream.

2. The church bell has not (rang, rung) today.

3. I haven't (drank, drunk) my hot chocolate.

4. We (knew, known) that it was time to go.

5. Have you (threw, thrown) the garbage out?

6. Haven't the movers (came, come) for our furniture?

7. We (rang, rung) the fire alarm five minutes ago.

8. Haven't you (know, known) him for a long time?

9. I (threw, thrown) the ball to James.

10. My friends from London, England, (came, come) this afternoon.

11. Why haven't you (drank, drunk) your juice?

12. I always (came, come) to work in my wheelchair now.

13. I (knew, known) Pat when she was just a child.

14. Have you (threw, thrown) away last week's newspaper?

15. We have (came, come) to tell you something.

16. If you already (rang, rung) the bell, then you might try knocking.

17. Tony thinks he (drank, drunk) something that made him ill.

B. Write a sentence using each verb below.

1. came _____

2. come _____

3. rang _____

4. rung _____

5. threw _____

6. thrown _____

7. drank _____

8. drunk _____

9. knew _____

Past Tenses of *Give*, *Take*, and *Write*

- Never use a helping verb with <u>gave</u>, <u>took</u>, and <u>wrote</u>.
- Always use a helping verb with <u>given</u>, <u>taken</u>, and <u>written</u>.

A. Underline the correct verb.

1. It (took, taken) the mechanic only a few minutes to change the tire.

2. Has anyone (took, taken) my note pad?

3. Who (wrote, written) the best letter?

4. I have (wrote, written) a thank-you note.

5. Tell me who (gave, given) you that address.

6. Have you (gave, given) the dog its food?

7. Bill hadn't (wrote, written) this poem.

8. Have you finally (wrote, written) for the tickets?

9. Emilio had (gave, given) the lecture on boat safety yesterday at the Y.M.C.A.

10. Alicia and I (wrote, written) a letter to the editor.

11. Haven't you (took, taken) your seat yet?

12. We had our picture (took, taken) yesterday.

13. Who (gave, given) you these old magazines?

14. The workers (took, taken) all their equipment with them.

15. A friend had (gave, given) us the furniture.

16. Leslie had (wrote, written) the letter over three weeks ago.

17. Who (took, taken) the most photographs on the trip?

18. The doctor (gave, given) me a tetanus shot after I cut my hand.

19. Has Brian (wrote, written) to Julia yet?

B. Write the correct past tense form of each verb in parentheses to complete the sentences.

1. (take) Amanda recently _____ her dog, Ralph, to the veterinarian.

2. (write) The doctor had _____ to say that Ralph needed his annual shots.

3. (give) An assistant _____ Ralph a dog biscuit as soon as he arrived.

4. (give) That way Ralph was _____ something that would distract him.

5. (take) Before Ralph knew it, the doctor had _____ a sample of his blood.

6. (take) It only _____ a minute to give Ralph his shots.

7. (give) The doctor _____ Ralph a pat on the head.

8. (take) "You have _____ very good care of Ralph," he said.

Eat, Fall, Draw, Drive, and Run

- Never use a helping verb with <u>ate</u>, <u>fell</u>, <u>drew</u>, <u>drove</u>, and <u>ran</u>.
- Always use a helping verb with <u>eaten</u>, <u>fallen</u>, <u>drawn</u>, <u>driven</u>, and <u>run</u>.

A. Underline the correct verb.

1. Taro, have you (drew, drawn) your diagram?

2. When we had (drove, driven) for two hours, we (began, begun) to feel hungry.

3. All of our pears have (fell, fallen) from the tree.

4. After we had (ate, eaten) our dinner, we (ran, run) around the lake.

5. A great architect (drew, drawn) the plans for our civic center.

6. We had just (ran, run) into the house when we saw our friends.

7. Hadn't the building already (fell, fallen) when you (ran, run) around the corner?

8. Those heavy curtains in the theater have (fell, fallen) down.

9. Last week we (drove, driven) to the lake for a vacation.

10. I have just (ate, eaten) a delicious slice of pizza.

11. I (ate, eaten) my breakfast before six o'clock this morning.

12. All of the leaves have (fell, fallen) from the elm trees.

13. When was the last time you (ran, run) a mile?

B. Write the correct past tense form of each verb in parentheses to complete the sentences.

1. (drive)   Last weekend we _____ to the lake for a picnic.

2. (draw)   Since Jenna knew several shortcuts, she _____ a detailed map for us.

3. (fall)   She mentioned that during a recent summer storm, debris had _____. on many of the roads.

4. (fall)   She warned us that a large tree _____ on one of the main roads.

5. (drive)   Jenna claimed that she had never _____ under such dangerous circumstances.

6. (run)   "I almost _____ right into that tree in the dark!" Jenna said.

7. (eat)   In order to avoid traveling at night, we _____ our dinner after we got home from the lake.

8. (eat)   We had _____ so much during our picnic that none of us minded waiting!

9. (draw)   Once home, we all agreed that Jenna had _____ a great map for us.

10. (run)   We made the trip in record time, and we hadn't _____ over any trees in the process!

- Never use a helping verb with <u>did</u>.
    - EXAMPLE: Anne **did** a great job on her test.
- Always use a helping verb with <u>done</u>.
    - EXAMPLE: Hallie **had** also **done** a great job.
- <u>Doesn't</u> is the contraction of <u>does not</u>. Use it with singular nouns and the pronouns <u>he</u>, <u>she</u>, and <u>it</u>.
    - EXAMPLES: Rachel **doesn't** want to go. It **doesn't** seem right.
- <u>Don't</u> is the contraction of <u>do not</u>. Use it with plural nouns and with the pronouns <u>I</u>, <u>you</u>, <u>we</u>, and <u>they</u>.
    - EXAMPLES: Mr. and Mrs. Ricci **don't** live there. You **don't** have your purse.

A. Underline the correct verb.

1. Why (doesn't, don't) Lois have the car keys?

2. Show me the way you (did, done) it.

3. Have the three of you (did, done) most of the work?

4. Why (doesn't, don't) she cash a check today?

5. Please show me what damage the storm (did, done).

6. (Doesn't, Don't) the workers on the morning shift do a fine job?

7. Have the new owners of our building (did, done) anything about the plumbing?

8. (Doesn't, Don't) those apples look overly ripe?

9. Chris (doesn't, don't) want to do the spring cleaning this week.

10. The gloves and the hat (doesn't, don't) match.

11. Carolyn, have you (did, done) your homework today?

12. Who (did, done) this fine job of painting?

13. (Doesn't, Don't) the tile in our new kitchen look nice?

14. (Doesn't, Don't) that dog stay in a fenced yard?

15. He has (did, done) me a great favor.

16. I will help if he (doesn't, don't).

B. Write one sentence using <u>did</u> and one sentence using <u>done</u>.

1. _____

2. _____

C. Write one sentence using <u>doesn't</u> and one sentence using <u>don't</u>.

1. _____

2. _____

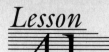
- **Mood** is a form of the verb that shows the manner of doing or being. There are three types of moods: **indicative, subjunctive,** and **imperative.**
- **Indicative mood** states a fact or asks a question.
  EXAMPLES: Ben **came** Friday. How many **went** to the meeting?
- **Subjunctive mood** can indicate a wish or a contrary-to-fact condition. Use <u>were</u> to express the subjunctive.
  EXAMPLE: I would help you, if I **were** able. (I am not able.)
- **Imperative mood** expresses a command or a request.
  EXAMPLES: **Ask** no more questions. Let's **start** immediately.

- **Give the mood of each underlined word.**

1. <u>Come</u> here at once. _____

2. I <u>did</u> not <u>see</u> Carolyn. _____

3. If I <u>were</u> not so tired, I would go to a movie. _____

4. <u>Call</u> for him at once. _____

5. Where <u>has</u> Brittany <u>moved</u>? _____

6. Who <u>invented</u> the sewing machine? _____

7. Juanita <u>came</u> Saturday. _____

8. Paul wishes it <u>were</u> true. _____

9. <u>Come</u> here, Jennifer. _____

10. I wish it <u>were</u> summer. _____

11. <u>Be</u> home early. _____

12. <u>Ring</u> the bell immediately. _____

13. The members of the band <u>sold</u> birthday calendars. _____

14. If I <u>were</u> you, I'd stop that. _____

15. Zachary <u>likes</u> my new sweater. _____

16. My friends <u>painted</u> the entire house. _____

17. If this <u>were</u> a sunny day, I would go with you. _____

18. <u>Tell</u> us where you went. _____

19. He greeted me as though I <u>were</u> a stranger. _____

Transitive and Intransitive Verbs

- There are two kinds of action verbs: **transitive** and **intransitive.**
- A transitive verb has a direct object.

D.O.

EXAMPLE: Jeffrey **painted** the house.
- An intransitive verb does not need an object to complete its meaning.

EXAMPLES: The sun **rises** in the east. She **walks** quickly.

A. Underline the verb in each sentence. Then write <u>T</u> for transitive or <u>I</u> for intransitive.

_____ 1. Kristina joined the health club in March.

_____ 2. She wanted the exercise to help her stay healthy.

_____ 3. Kristina exercised every day after work.

_____ 4. She became friends with Nancy.

_____ 5. They worked out together.

_____ 6. Nancy preferred the treadmill.

_____ 7. Kristina liked aerobics and running.

_____ 8. Sometimes they switched activities.

_____ 9. Nancy took an aerobics class.

_____ 10. Kristina used the treadmill.

_____ 11. Occasionally they swam in the pool.

_____ 12. Nancy was the better swimmer.

_____ 13. But Kristina had more fun.

_____ 14. She just splashed around in the water.

B. Underline the transitive verb, and circle the direct object in each sentence.

1. Carlos walked Tiny every day.

2. Tiny usually pulled Carlos along.

3. Carlos washed Tiny every other week.

4. Tiny loved water.

5. He splashed Carlos whenever he could.

6. Tiny also loved rawhide bones.

7. He chewed the bones until they were gone.

8. Carlos found Tiny when Tiny was just a puppy.

Active and Passive Voice

- **Voice** refers to the relation of a subject to its verb.
- In the **active voice,** the subject acts.
  - EXAMPLE: **I painted** the house.
- In the **passive voice,** the subject receives the action.
  - EXAMPLE: The house **was painted** by me.
- Only transitive verbs are used in the passive voice.

A. Write **A** if the sentence is in the active voice and **P** if it is in the passive voice.

_____ **1.** Marty applied for a job in a grocery store.

_____ **2.** He needs money for gas and car repairs.

_____ **3.** He will handle the cash register.

_____ **4.** Marty will also stock the shelves.

_____ **5.** The application was turned in last week.

_____ **6.** The store's manager reads every application.

_____ **7.** Then the applicants are interviewed.

_____ **8.** Marty was interviewed on Monday.

_____ **9.** The manager was impressed by Marty.

_____ **10.** He will give Marty the job.

B. Rewrite each sentence in the active voice.

1. Kate was given a job babysitting by the McNeils.

_____

2. The children will be watched by her every day.

_____

3. Kate will be driven to their house by her friend.

_____

C. Rewrite each sentence in the passive voice.

1. Trina plays the drums in the band.

_____

2. She chose the drums because her father played drums.

_____

3. Trina won an award for her playing.

_____

> - A **gerund** is the present participle of a verb form ending in <u>-ing</u> that is used as a noun.
> - A gerund may be the subject, direct object, or object of a preposition.
>   EXAMPLES: **Exercising** is vital to good health. (subject)
>   Tanya enjoys **exercising**. (direct object)
>   I have thought of **exercising**. (object of preposition)

■ **Underline each gerund.**

1. We enjoy <u>living</u> on the farm.

2. Airplanes are used in fighting forest fires.

3. Landing an airplane requires skill.

4. Climbing Pikes Peak is quite an experience.

5. The moaning of the wind through the pines lulled me to sleep.

6. The dog's barking awakened everyone in the house.

7. Keeping his temper is difficult for John.

8. Sue objected to our hanging the picture in this room.

9. Laughing aloud is encouraged by the comedian.

10. Being treasurer of this club is a responsibility.

11. Making a speech makes me nervous.

12. Winning this game will place our soccer team first in the league.

13. It was my first attempt at pitching horseshoes.

14. Rapid eating will make digestion difficult.

15. Playing golf is a favorite pastime in many countries.

16. Planning a party requires much thought.

17. We have completed our packing for the trip to the mountains.

18. The howling of the dogs disturbed our sleep.

19. I am tired of doing this work.

20. We are fond of living here.

21. Native Americans once spent much time planting, hunting, and fishing.

22. Neat writing is important in school.

23. I enjoy skating on this pond.

24. Jason taught us the rules of boating.

25. Pressing the wrong button can be very dangerous.

26. Airplanes are used in the mapping of large areas.

27. Swimming in this lake is my favorite sport.

28. I enjoy driving a car.

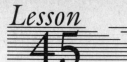

■ An **infinitive** is the base form of the verb, commonly preceded by <u>to</u>.
■ An infinitive may be used as a noun, adverb, or adjective.
    EXAMPLES: **To know** him is **to like** him. (noun) She came here **to study.** (adverb) That is the movie **to see.** (adjective)

■ **Underline each infinitive.**

1. I want <u>to go</u> home before it gets any colder.

2. We went to see the play while Emilio was here.

3. I prepared the salad to serve for lunch.

4. To shoot firecrackers in the city limits is against the law in some places.

5. I like to walk in the country.

6. They were taught to stand, to sit, to walk, and to dance gracefully.

7. Gradually people learned to use fire and to make tools.

8. I need to get a new coat.

9. We plan to make the trip in four hours.

10. Carol, are you too tired to clean the kitchen?

11. Jack, try to be on time in the morning.

12. Anthony plans to travel in Canada during August.

13. Who taught you to play golf?

14. We were taught to rise early.

15. We were hoping to see you at the reunion.

16. Pay one fee to enter the amusement park.

17. Jennifer, I forgot to mail your package.

18. To cook this turkey will require several hours.

19. The children ran to meet their friend.

20. We are learning to speak Spanish.

21. We are planning to exhibit our artwork next week.

22. To succeed as an artist was Rick's dream.

23. We went to see the parade.

24. We are ready to eat.

25. It was easy to see the reason for that actor's popularity.

26. The only way to have a friend is to be one.

27. Madame Curie was the only woman to receive the Nobel Prize a second time.

28. To score the most points is the object of the game.

29. We need to go grocery shopping.

30. Do you want to paint the fence on Saturday?

> ■ A **present** or **past participle** is a verb form that may be used as an adjective.
>
> EXAMPLES: A **dripping** faucet can be a nuisance. **Wilted** flowers were removed from the vase.

■ **Underline each participle.**

1. We saw a running deer in the forest.

2. The chart showing sales figures is very helpful.

3. The scampering cat ran to the nearest tree.

4. A team of deep-sea divers discovered the hidden treasure.

5. We saw the thunderstorm advancing across the plains.

6. Biting insects hovered over our campsite at night.

7. His foot, struck by the falling timbers, was injured.

8. The whispering pines filled the air with their fresh scent.

9. People preparing for a career in aviation should master mathematics.

10. We drove slowly, enjoying every minute of the drive.

11. Onions are among the largest vegetable crops produced in the United States.

12. The truck, burdened with its load, traveled slowly over the rough road.

13. Jan, thinking about her new job, was very happy.

14. Several passengers injured in the wreck were brought to the local hospital.

15. That expanding city will soon be the largest one in the state.

16. The fire, fanned by the high winds, threatened the entire area.

17. The rude person, shoving others aside, went to see the manager.

18. The lake, frozen solidly, looked like a huge mirror.

19. The man playing the trombone is my brother.

20. The cleaned apartment was ready for new tenants.

21. Teasing children ran at Rip Van Winkle's heels.

22. Balloons lifting weather instruments are released daily by many weather stations.

23. The chirping bird flew from tree to tree.

24. The surviving pilot described the accident.

25. The dedicated artist worked patiently.

26. Homing pigeons were used in the experiment.

27. The whistling youngster skipped happily down the road.

28. Ironed shirts were stacked neatly at the cleaners.

29. Those standing near the fence should form a second line.

30. The child ran to his loving father, who comforted him.

- Use <u>may</u> to ask for permission.
  EXAMPLE: **May** I go with you?
- Use <u>can</u> to express the ability to do something.
  EXAMPLE: James **can** swim well.

A. Complete each sentence with <u>may</u> or <u>can</u>.

1. Adam, _____ you whistle?

2. His dog _____ do three difficult tricks.

3. Miss Nance, _____ I leave work early?

4. I _____ see the airplane in the distance.

5. Chris, _____ you tie a good knot?

6. Carlos, _____ I drive your car?

7. You _____ see the mountains from here.

8. My friend _____ drive us home.

9. The Garcias _____ speak three languages.

10. _____ I examine those new books?

- Teach means "to give instruction."
  EXAMPLE: I'll **teach** you how to shoot free throws.
- Learn means "to acquire knowledge."
  EXAMPLE: When did you **learn** to speak Spanish?

B. Complete each sentence with <u>teach</u> or <u>learn</u>.

1. I think he will _____ me quickly.

2. I will _____ to recite that poem.

3. Did Jamie _____ you to build a fire?

4. The women are going to _____ to use the new machines.

5. Will you _____ me to play tennis?

6. My brother is going to _____ Billy to skate.

7. Would you like to _____ the rules of the game to them?

8. No one can _____ you if you do not try to _____.

- Sit means "to take a resting position." Its principal parts are sit, sitting, and sat.
  EXAMPLES: Please **sit** here. He **sat** beside her.
- Set means "to place." Its principal parts are set, setting, and set.
  EXAMPLES: Will you please **set** this dish on the table?
  She **set** the table for dinner last night.

A. Underline the correct verb.

1. Please (sit, set) down, Kathleen.

2. Where should we (sit, set) the television?

3. Where do you (sit, set)?

4. Pamela, please (sit, set) those plants out this afternoon.

5. (Sit, Set) the basket of groceries on the patio.

6. José usually (sits, sets) on this side of the table.

7. Please come and (sit, set) your books down on that desk.

8. Have you ever (sat, set) by this window?

9. Does he (sit, set) in this seat?

10. Why don't you (sit, set) over here?

- Lie means "to recline" or "to occupy a certain space." Its principal parts are lie, lying, lay, and lain.
  EXAMPLES: Why don't you **lie** down for a while?
  He **has lain** in the hammock all afternoon.
- Lay means "to place." Its principal parts are lay, laying, and laid.
  EXAMPLES: The men **are laying** new carpeting in the house.
  Who **laid** the wet towel on the table?

B. Underline the correct verb.

1. Where did you (lie, lay) your gloves, Beth?

2. (Lie, Lay) down, Spot.

3. He always (lies, lays) down to rest when he is very tired.

4. Where have you (lain, laid) the evening paper?

5. Please (lie, lay) this box on the desk.

6. Do not (lie, lay) on that dusty hay.

7. (Lay, Lie) the papers on top of the desk.

8. I (laid, lain) the shovel on that pile of dirt.

9. I need to (lie, lay) down to rest.

10. She has (laid, lain) on the sofa all morning.

Lesson 49 — Pronouns

> - A **pronoun** is a word used in place of a noun.
> - A **personal pronoun** is chosen based on the way it is used in the sentence.
>   A **subject pronoun** is used in the subject of a sentence and after a linking verb.
>   EXAMPLES: **He** is a chemist. The chemist is **he**.
>   An **object pronoun** is used after an action verb or a preposition.
>   EXAMPLES: Jan gave **me** the gift. Jan gave the gift to **me**.
>   A **possessive pronoun** is used to show ownership of something.
>   EXAMPLES: The new car is **ours**. That is **our** car.

■ **Underline each pronoun.**

1. Brian, do you have my ticket to the play?

2. Just between you and me, I want to go with them.

3. Carol, will you help me carry our trunk?

4. May I go with you?

5. We saw him standing in line to go to a movie.

6. Just be sure to find Carol and me.

7. We will be ready when they come for us.

8. She sent this box of frozen steaks to Andrea and me.

9. She asked you and me to be on her bowling team.

10. We saw them go into the building on the corner.

11. Last week we sent flowers to our sick friend.

12. He must choose their dinner.

13. She is my English instructor.

14. They have never invited us to go with them.

15. The first-place winner is she.

16. Can he compete against you?

17. She made the dinner for us.

18. Liz and I are going on vacation in June.

19. Where is your umbrella?

20. Sharon gave me a book to read.

21. Do you know where our cottage is?

22. If I lend you my car, will you take care of it?

23. I gave him my word that we would visit her.

24. When they saw us fishing, Bob and Diane changed their clothes.

25. Your toes are peeking through your socks.

26. Marie showed us how to fasten her bike to our car.

Lesson 50

Demonstrative and Indefinite Pronouns

> - A **demonstrative pronoun** is used to point out a specific person or thing.
> - This and that are used in place of singular nouns. This refers to a person or thing nearby, and that refers to a person or thing farther away.
>   EXAMPLES: **This** is mine. **That** is the right one.
> - These and those are used in place of plural nouns. These points to persons or things nearby, and those points to persons or things farther away.
>   EXAMPLES: **These** are the best ones. **Those** don't look ripe.

A. Underline each demonstrative pronoun.

1. Those are the books I lost.

2. That is where Anne lives.

3. I'm not sure these are my scissors.

4. This is my pen; that is Pam's book.

5. I think those are interesting books.

6. Is that your first mistake?

7. This is Gretchen's timecard.

8. Give these to your friend.

9. These are Stephanie's shoes.

10. Please don't mention this.

11. I think those are just rumors.

12. Will this be our last chance?

13. Dave, those are your messages.

14. These are large peaches.

15. Sorry, that was my last piece.

16. Who told you that?

> - An **indefinite pronoun** does not refer to a specific person or thing.
>   EXAMPLE: **Many** are called, but **few** are chosen.
> - The indefinite pronouns anybody, anyone, anything, each, everyone, everybody, everything, nobody, no one, nothing, one, somebody, someone, and something are singular. They take singular verbs.
>   EXAMPLE: **Everyone is** ready.
> - The indefinite pronouns both, few, many, several, and some are plural. They take plural verbs.
>   EXAMPLE: **Several are** ready.

B. Underline each indefinite pronoun.

1. Both worked hard.

2. Let each help decorate.

3. Several have called about the job.

4. Unfortunately, some never learn.

5. Everyone was delighted at our party.

6. I think someone forgot this sweater.

7. Some asked for pens.

8. He thinks that each is right.

9. Has anyone seen my wallet?

10. Will someone wash the dishes?

11. Both of the singers are here.

12. One is absent.

13. Each must carry a bag.

14. Some always succeed.

15. Did someone leave this lunch?

16. Everybody is to be here early.

- An **antecedent** is the word to which a pronoun refers.
    EXAMPLE: **Stars** are lovely when **they** shine.
- A pronoun must agree with its antecedent in **gender (masculine, feminine,** or **neuter)** and **number (singular** or **plural).**
    EXAMPLES: **Susan** helped **her** friend. The **people** went in **their** cars.
- If the antecedent is an indefinite pronoun, it is correct to use a masculine pronoun. However, it is now common to use both a masculine and feminine pronoun.
    EXAMPLES: **Someone** lost **his** dog. **Someone** lost **his or her** dog.

■ **Underline the correct pronoun, and circle its antecedent.**

1. (Everyone) should work hard at (their, <u>his or her</u>) job.

2. Each of the children willingly did (his or her, their) share of the camp duties.

3. Sophia gave me (her, their) coat to wear.

4. I took (my, our) friend to the ceremony.

5. All members were asked to bring (his or her, their) contributions today.

6. The women have had (her, their) vacation.

7. Someone has left (her or his, their) automobile across the driveway.

8. If each does (his or her, their) best, our chorus will win.

9. Would you tell Joanne that (her, his) soup is ready?

10. Every woman did (her, their) best to make the program a success.

11. Never judge anyone entirely by (his or her, their) looks.

12. Each student should do (his or her, their) own work.

13. I lost (my, our) favorite earring at the dance.

14. Each woman takes (her, their) own equipment on the camping trip.

15. Each one has a right to (his or her, their) own opinion in this matter.

16. (His, Her) sense of humor is what I like best about Joseph.

17. Some man has left (his, their) raincoat.

18. The two waiters dropped (his, their) trays when they bumped into each other.

19. Has each student received (his or her, their) report card?

20. Every person is expected to do (her or his, their) best.

21. We knew that every man at the meeting expressed (his, their) opinion.

22. Every woman furnishes (her, their) own transportation.

23. Jeff and Tom found (his, their) cabin in the dark.

24. Cliff brings his dog every time (he, she) visits.

25. The bird was in (their, its) nest.

26. Mark read (his, her) final essay for me.

Lesson 52

Relative Pronouns

> - A **relative pronoun** is a pronoun that can introduce a subordinate clause. The relative pronouns are who, whom, whose (referring to persons); which (referring to things); and that (referring to persons or things).
> - A **subordinate clause**, when introduced by a relative pronoun, serves as an adjective. It modifies a word, or antecedent, in the main clause.
>   EXAMPLES: Tom knows the author **whose** articles we read in class. The family for **whom** I work is from Canada. The movie **that** won the prize is playing.

A. Write t

  1. mou

  2. wea

  3. jour

  4. clas

  5. boo

- Co
  in

B. Under

  1. Th

  2. W

  3. Tl

  4. Tl

  5. T

  6. T

  7. T

  8. V

  9. T

 10. D

 11. V

 12. /

 13. T

 14. /

 15.

 16.

 17.

 18.

■ **Underline each relative pronoun, and circle its antecedent.**

  1. The (letter) that was published in our daily paper was very long.

  2. It was Karen who sang the most difficult song.

  3. Robert Burns, who wrote "My Heart's in the Highlands," was Scottish.

  4. It was Sylvia who wanted Zach's address.

  5. The shop that was filled with video games is going out of business.

  6. My parents live in a New England farmhouse that was built many years ago.

  7. This is the pearl that is so valuable.

  8. The bridge, which is made of wood, was built two hundred years ago.

  9. Did you see the animal that ran across the road?

 10. Good roads have opened up many regions that were formerly impassable.

 11. For our Thanksgiving dinner, we had a turkey that weighed twenty pounds.

 12. This story, which was written by Eudora Welty, is most interesting.

 13. Anna is a person whom you can trust.

 14. We ate the delicious hamburgers that Andrew had prepared.

 15. Food that is eaten in pleasant surroundings is usually digested easily.

 16. This is the first painting that I did.

 17. The sweater that you want is too expensive.

 18. She is the one whom we watched at the track meet.

 19. The only money that they spent was for food.

 20. Your friend is one person who is inconsiderate.

 21. A rare animal that lives in our city zoo was featured on the evening news.

 22. Heather is one of the guests whom I invited.

 23. Is this the file for which you've been searching?

 24. Leonardo da Vinci is the artist whose work they most admire.

 25. The science museum is an attraction that is visited by many tourists.

 26. Charles Dickens is a writer whom I've read extensively.

Unit 3,   Unit 3, (

57 Adverns

> ■ An **adverb** is a word that modifies a verb, an adjective, or another adverb.
> EXAMPLES: The rain poured **steadily.** His memories were **extremely** vivid. She responded **very** quickly.
> ■ An adverb usually tells **how, when, where,** or **how often.**
> ■ Many adverbs end in -ly.

A. Underline each adverb.

1. The person read slowly but clearly and expressively.

2. Adam, you are driving too recklessly.

3. The airplane started moving slowly but quickly gained speed.

4. I spoke too harshly to my friends.

5. How did all of you get here?

6. I looked everywhere for my pen.

7. The man stopped suddenly and quickly turned around.

8. Stacy read that poem too rapidly.

9. Janice plays the guitar well.

10. The child was sleeping soundly.

11. The car was running noisily.

12. We returned early.

13. Those trees were severely damaged in the fire.

14. Jack ran quickly, but steadily, in the race.

B. Write two adverbs that could be used to modify each verb.

1. read _____ _____

2. think _____ _____

3. walk _____ _____

4. eat _____ _____

5. sing _____ _____

6. speak _____ _____

7. dive _____ _____

8. study _____ _____

9. write _____ _____

10. look _____ _____

Comparing with Adverbs

- An **adverb** has three degrees of comparison: **positive, comparative,** and **superlative.**
- The simple form of the adverb is called the **positive** degree.
  EXAMPLE: Kathy ran **fast** in the race.
- When two actions are being compared, the **comparative** degree is used.
  EXAMPLE: Amy ran **faster** than Kathy.
- When three or more actions are being compared, the **superlative** degree is used.
  EXAMPLE: Maureen ran the **fastest** of all.
- Use -er to form the comparative degree and use -est to form the superlative degree of one-syllable adverbs.
- Use more or most with longer adverbs and with adverbs that end in -ly.
  EXAMPLES: Louisa ran **more energetically** than Bob.
  Ms. Baker ran the **most energetically** of all the runners.

A. Underline the adverb that best completes each sentence.

1. Mark arrived (sooner, soonest) than Greg.

2. Tony arrived the (sooner, soonest) of all.

3. They had to work very (hard, harder, hardest).

4. Tony painted (more, most) carefully than Mark.

5. Mark worked (faster, fastest) than Greg, so Mark painted the walls.

6. Lauren worked the (more, most) carefully of all.

B. Complete each sentence with the proper form of the adverb in parentheses.

1. (fast)   Jason wanted to be the _____ runner at our school.

2. (fast)   Juan could run _____ than Jason.

3. (seriously)   Jason trained _____ than he had before.

4. (frequently)   Jason is on the track _____ of all the runners.

5. (quickly)   Jason ran the sprint _____ than he did yesterday.

6. (promptly)   Jason arrives for practice _____ of anyone on the team.

7. (promptly)   He even arrives _____ than the coach!

8. (eagerly)   Juan does warm-up exercises _____ of all the runners.

9. (carefully)   Who concentrates _____ on his timing, Juan or Jason?

10. (hard)   The coach congratulates Jason on being the player who works the

_____ .

■ **Underline the correct word.**

1. Always drive very (careful, carefully).

2. The lake seems (calm, calmly) today.

3. The storm raged (furious, furiously).

4. The dog waited (patient, patiently) for its owner.

5. Nicole's letters are always (cheerful, cheerfully) written.

6. Although our team played (good, well), we lost the game.

7. Always answer your mail (prompt, promptly).

8. James speaks (respectful, respectfully) to everyone.

9. Tara is (happy, happily) with her new work.

10. Write this address (legible, legibly).

11. The time passed (slow, slowly).

12. The robin chirped (happy, happily) from its nest.

13. We were (sure, surely) glad to hear from him.

14. Rebecca tries to do her work (good, well).

15. I think Brenda will (easy, easily) win that contest.

16. We had to talk (loud, loudly) to be heard.

17. Yesterday the sun shone (bright, brightly) all day.

18. He says he sleeps (good, well) every night.

19. The elevator went up (quick, quickly) to the top floor.

20. The storm began very (sudden, suddenly).

21. You did react very (cautious, cautiously).

22. Every student should do this work (accurate, accurately).

23. Eric rode his bike (furious, furiously) to get home on time.

24. The paint on the house is (new, newly).

25. The mist fell (steady, steadily) all evening.

26. The river looked (beautiful, beautifully) in the moonlight.

27. The salesperson always answers questions (courteous, courteously).

28. He always does (good, well) when selling that product.

29. Ryan can swim (good, well).

30. I was (real, really) excited about going to San Francisco.

31. I think he talks (foolish, foolishly).

32. It seems (foolish, foolishly) to me.

33. That bell rang too (loud, loudly) for this small room.

34. Our grass seems to grow very (rapid, rapidly).

Prepositions

> - A **preposition** is a word that shows the relationship of a noun or a pronoun to another word in the sentence.
>   EXAMPLES: Put the package **on** the table. Place the package **in** the desk.
> - These are some commonly used prepositions:
>
> | about | against | at | between | from | of | through | under |
> |-------|---------|-----|---------|------|-----|---------|-------|
> | above | among | behind | by | in | on | to | upon |
> | across | around | beside | for | into | over | toward | with |

- **Draw a line under each preposition or prepositions in the sentences below.**

1. The grin on Juan's face was bright and warm.

2. He greeted his cousin from Brazil with a smile and a handshake.

3. They walked through the airport and toward the baggage area.

4. Juan found his bags between two boxes.

5. The two cousins had not seen each other for five years.

6. They could spend hours talking about everything.

7. Juan and Luis got into Juan's truck.

8. Juan drove Luis to Juan's family's ranch.

9. It was a long ride across many hills and fields.

10. Luis rested his head against the seat.

11. Soon they drove over a hill and into a valley.

12. The ranch was located across the Harrison River.

13. The house stood among a group of oak trees.

14. Juan parked the truck beside the driveway.

15. They walked across the driveway and toward the house.

16. Juan's mother, Anita, stood behind the screen door.

17. Juan's family gathered around Luis.

18. Everyone sat on the porch and drank lemonade.

19. "Tell us about our relatives in Brazil," Rosa asked.

20. "You have over twenty cousins in my area," said Luis.

21. They go to school, just like you do.

22. Then everyone went into the house and ate dinner.

23. Juan's family passed the food across the table.

24. "Many of these dishes come from old family recipes," he said.

25. "It is wonderful to be among so many relatives," Luis said.

26. After dinner, everyone went to the living room.

27. Luis showed them photographs of his home in Brazil.

Prepositional Phrases

- A **phrase** is a group of closely related words used as a single part of speech but not containing a subject and predicate.
  EXAMPLE: The writer **of this novel** is signing autographs.
- A **prepositional phrase** is a group of words that begins with a preposition and ends with a noun or pronoun.
  EXAMPLE: He took the train **to New York.**
- The noun or pronoun in the prepositional phrase is called the **object of the preposition.**
  EXAMPLE: He took the train to **New York.**

- **Put parentheses around each prepositional phrase. Then underline each preposition, and circle the object of the preposition.**

1. The airplane was flying (above the clouds).

2. We are moving to North Carolina.

3. Sandra lives on the second block.

4. An old water tower once stood on that hill.

5. The car slid on the wet pavement.

6. Sealing wax was invented in the seventeenth century.

7. Motto rings were first used by the Romans.

8. Tungsten, a metal, was discovered in 1781.

9. Roses originally came from Asia.

10. The ball rolled into the street.

11. Do you always keep the puppies in a pen?

12. The children climbed over the fence.

13. She lives in Denver, Colorado.

14. Columbus made three trips to North America.

15. They spread the lunch under the shade of the giant elm tree.

16. The treasure was found by a scuba diver.

17. A squad of soldiers marched behind the tank.

18. Shall I row across the stream?

19. Large airplanes fly across the nation.

20. Walter looked into the sack.

21. The cat ran up the pole.

22. We visited the Alexander Graham Bell Museum in Nova Scotia.

23. Many tourists come to our region.

24. We spent last summer in the Adirondack Mountains.

25. Do not stand behind a parked car.

> ■ A prepositional phrase can be used to describe a noun or a pronoun.
> Then the prepositional phrase is being used as an **adjective** to tell
> which one, what kind, or how many.
> EXAMPLE: The bird **in the tree** whistled.
> The prepositional phrase <u>in the tree</u> tells **which** bird.
> ■ A prepositional phrase can be used to describe a verb. Then the prepositional
> phrase is being used as an **adverb** to tell how, where, or when.
> EXAMPLE: Charlie ate breakfast **before leaving for school.**
> The prepositional phrase **before leaving for school** tells **when**
> Charlie ate breakfast.

■ **Underline each prepositional phrase, and classify it as adjective or adverb.**

1. They went <u>to the ranch</u>.   *adv.*

2. The first savings bank was established in France.

3. Fall Creek Falls in Tennessee is my home.

4. Return all books to the public library.

5. Mark lives in an old house.

6. Tanya bought a sweater with red trim.

7. The birds in the zoo are magnificent.

8. Jade is found in Burma.

9. I spent the remainder of my money.

10. The magician waved a wand over the hat, and a rabbit appeared.

11. The diameter of a Sequoia tree trunk can reach ten feet.

12. The capital of New York is Albany.

13. The narrowest streets are near the docks.

14. Our family went to the movie.

15. Roald Amundsen discovered the South Pole in 1911.

16. The floor in this room is painted black.

17. The dead leaves are blowing across the yard.

18. A forest of petrified wood has been found.

19. The mole's tunnel runs across the lawn.

Conjunctions

> - A **conjunction** is a word used to join words or groups of words.
>   EXAMPLE: Jenna **and** her sister are in Arizona.
> - These are some commonly used conjunctions:
>
> | although | because | however | or | that | when | while |
> |----------|---------|---------|----|------|------|-------|
> | and | but | if | since | though | whereas | yet |
> | as | for | nor | than | unless | whether | |
>
> - Some conjunctions are used in pairs. These include either . . .or, neither . . . nor, and not only . . . but also.

- **Underline each conjunction.**

1. He and I are friends.

2. David likes tennis, whereas Jim prefers running.

3. We had to wait since it was raining.

4. We left early, but we missed the train.

5. The show was not only long but also boring.

6. Neither the chairs nor the tables had been dusted.

7. Hail and sleet fell during the storm.

8. Neither Carmen nor Kara was able to attend the meeting.

9. I have neither time nor energy to waste.

10. Bowling and tennis are my favorite sports.

11. Either Dan or Don will bring a portable radio.

12. The people in the car and the people in the van exchanged greetings.

13. Neither cookies nor cake is on your diet.

14. Although I like to take photographs, I am not a good photographer.

15. Did you see Charles when he visited here?

16. We are packing our bags since our vacation trip begins tomorrow.

17. She cannot concentrate while you are making so much noise.

18. Unless you hurry, the party will be over before you arrive.

19. We enjoyed the visit although we were very tired.

20. Both mammals and birds are warm-blooded.

21. She is one performer who can both sing and dance.

22. Unless you have some objections, I will submit this report.

23. Neither dogs nor cats are allowed in this park.

24. April watered the plants while Luis mowed the lawn.

25. I will see you when you are feeling better.

26. Either Ms. Andretti or Ms. Garcia will teach that course.

27. We got here late because we lost our directions.

Double Negatives

> ■ The **adverbs** <u>not</u>, <u>never</u>, <u>hardly</u>, <u>scarcely</u>, <u>seldom</u>, <u>none</u>, and <u>nothing</u> should not be used with a negative verb. One clause cannot properly contain two negatives.
>
> EXAMPLES: There wasn't anything left in the refrigerator. (Correct)
> There wasn't nothing left in the refrigerator. (Incorrect)

■ **Underline the correct word.**

1. We couldn't see (anything, nothing) through the fog.

2. The suspect wouldn't admit (anything, nothing).

3. I don't know (any, none) of the people on this bus.

4. Rosa couldn't do (anything, nothing) about changing the time of our program.

5. We didn't have (any, no) printed programs.

6. I don't want (any, no) cereal for breakfast this morning.

7. You must not speak to (anyone, no one) about our surprise party plans.

8. There isn't (any, no) ink in this pen.

9. Didn't you make (any, no) copies for the other people?

10. I haven't had (any, no) time to repair the lawn mower.

11. She hasn't said (anything, nothing) about her accident.

12. Hardly (anything, nothing) pleases him.

13. There aren't (any, no) pears in this supermarket.

14. There isn't (any, no) newspaper in that little town.

15. There wasn't (anybody, nobody) in the house.

16. Please don't ask him (any, no) questions.

17. I haven't solved (any, none) of my problems.

18. I haven't done (anything, nothing) to offend Greg.

19. We don't have (any, no) water pressure.

20. Our team wasn't (any, no) match for the opposing team.

21. I couldn't hear (anything, nothing) because of the airplane's noise.

22. The salesperson didn't have (any, no) samples on display.

23. I haven't (any, no) money with me.

24. Hasn't he cooked (any, none) of the pasta?

25. We haven't (any, no) more packages to wrap.

26. Wasn't there (anyone, no one) at home?

27. My dog has never harmed (anybody, nobody).

28. They seldom have (anyone, no one) absent from their meetings.

29. There weren't (any, no) clouds in the sky.

Review

A. Write the part of speech above each underlined word. Use the abbreviations given in the box.

1. A heavy dust storm rolled across the prairie.

2. This is a nice surprise!

3. The dark clouds slowly gathered in the north.

4. Marlee and I are showing slides of the photographs that we took on our trip.

5. Is the capital of your state built on a river?

6. These shrubs are beautiful.

7. Someone opened the door very cautiously and tiptoed inside.

8. Please handle this extremely fragile china very carefully.

9. The weary people waited for the long parade to start.

10. Large herds of longhorn cattle grazed on these vast plains.

11. We are going to the new mall today, but Sara can't go with us.

12. Floyd, you are eating that food too rapidly.

n.	noun
pron.	pronoun
v.	verb
adj.	adjective
adv.	adverb
prep.	preposition
conj.	conjunction

B. Write the plural form or the possessive form of the noun in parentheses.

1. (bench)   The park _____ need to be painted.

2. (fly)   The _____ landed on our picnic lunch.

3. (hero)   All of the _____ medals were awarded at the ceremony.

4. (pony)   Her _____ saddle has been cleaned and oiled.

5. (watch)   My _____ hands stopped moving.

C. Underline the appositive or appositive phrase, and circle the noun it identifies.

1. We plan to visit Ottawa, the capital of Canada, on our vacation.

2. My older sister Kira is an engineer.

3. We ate a hearty breakfast, pancakes and ham, before going to work.

D. Circle the correct verb.

1. A former resident (gave, given) this fountain to the city.

2. Was it the telephone or the doorbell that (rang, rung)?

3. Our guest speaker has (come, came) a little early.

4. Caroline has (know, known) Paul for ten years.

5. We asked Jan to (drive, driven) us to the movies.

6. Matt, haven't you (ate, eaten) the last piece of pineapple cake?

7. The frightened deer (ran, run) into the forest.

8. The Arnolds (gone, went) to Florida last January.

9. Andy (doesn't, don't) like to be late to work.

10. Chloe (took, taken) her brother to the zoo.

11. Susan (did, done) all of her chores before we went to the movie.

12. Jessica and I (is, are) ready to go, too.

13. Many of the trout (was, were) returned to the stream after the contest.

14. I have (began, begun) the study of Spanish.

15. A dead silence had (fell, fallen) upon the listeners.

16. Larry (wasn't, weren't) at work this morning.

E. Underline the verbal in each sentence, and write infinitive, participle, or gerund on the line.

_____ 1. The reason they went to the lake was to fish.

_____ 2. Skating has become a popular sport.

_____ 3. The flashing lights warned people of danger.

_____ 4. Juan's goal is to finish law school.

_____ 5. The improved detergent cleaned better than the old formula.

F. Underline the pronoun in parentheses that agrees with the antecedent. Circle the antecedent.

1. Curtis and Erika tutored Mark because (he, they) had missed the review.

2. The office workers had to leave (their, its) building when a fire started.

3. Bob and Andre brought the posters to (them, their) campaign office.

4. My sister collected baskets on (her, their) trip to Mexico.

5. The volunteers accepted donations and gave (it, them) to the charity.

A. Read the following paragraphs.

   Tibet, which is a remote land in south-central Asia, is often called the Roof of
the World or Land of the Snows. Its mountains and plateaus are the highest in the
world. The capital of Tibet, Lhasa, is 12,000 feet high.

   Tibetans, who are sometimes called the hermit people, follow a simple way of
life. They are a short and sturdy people and do heavy physical work. Some
are nomads, herders who roam about in the northern uplands of the country.
Once a year, the nomads come to the low regions to sell their products
and to buy things that they need. They live in tents made of yak hair. A yak is
about the size of a small ox and has long hair. Yaks are good companions to the
nomads because they can live and work in the high altitudes.

B. Write two appositives from the paragraph above.

_____   _____

C. Write four relative pronouns and their antecedents.

1. _____   _____   3. _____   _____

2. _____   _____   4. _____   _____

D. Write three prepositional phrases.

1. _____

2. _____

3. _____

E. Write one superlative adjective.

_____

F. Write one indefinite pronoun.

_____

G. Write two intransitive verbs.

_____   _____

H. Write two infinitives.

_____   _____

I. Write two conjunctions.

_____   _____

J. Read the following paragraphs.

If you were to guess which people were the first to learn to write, would you guess the Egyptians? Experts believe thousands of years ago, around 3100 B.C., Egyptians first began writing. Much of their writing was done to record historical events. Later, writings were used on pyramids to ensure peace for the kings buried in them. The writings were in hieroglyphics, a system of writing based on pictures.

Egyptian pyramids are notable for a number of reasons. The oldest pyramid is called Saqqarah. It was built with hundreds of steps running up to the top and was the first building in the country made entirely of stone. It clearly shows how advanced the ancient Egyptian culture was, both artistically and mechanically.

Another incredible monument is the Great Sphinx—a half-lion, half-man stone structure built for King Khafre. Historians have been able to learn much about the ancient Egyptian people by studying these buildings and the materials in them. Fortunately, the climate in Egypt was dry, so the writings and artifacts were well-preserved.

K. Write a subjunctive verb from the paragraph above.

_____

L. Write two adverbs.

_____   _____

M. Write two passive verbs.

_____   _____

N. Write an appositive.

_____

O. Write two abstract nouns.

_____   _____

P. Write two concrete nouns.

_____   _____

Q. Write two conjunctions.

_____   _____

R. Write two prepositional phrases.

_____

_____

Using Capital Letters

> - **Capitalize** the first word of a sentence and of each line of poetry.
>   EXAMPLES: Jim recited a poem. The first two lines follow.
>   All the animals looked up in wonder
>   When they heard the roaring thunder.
> - Capitalize the first word of a direct quotation.
>   EXAMPLE: Beth said, "Let's try to memorize a poem, too."
> - Capitalize the first, last, and all important words in the titles of books, poems, stories, and songs.
>   EXAMPLES: *The Jungle Book,* "Snow Time"

A. Circle each letter that should be capitalized. Write the capital letter above it.

1. Anthony said, "what time does the movie start?"

2. francis Scott Key wrote "the star spangled banner."

3. edgar Allan Poe, the author of "the raven," was born in Boston.

4. paul asked, "when do you plan to visit your friend?"

5. who wrote the poems "snowbound" and "the barefoot boy"?

6. what famous American said, "give me liberty, or give me death"?

> - Capitalize all **proper nouns.**
>   EXAMPLES: James T. White, Mother, Fifth Avenue, Italy, Missouri
>   Smokey Mountains, Thanksgiving, November, Statue of Liberty,
>   *Mayflower,* British Columbia
> - Capitalize all **proper adjectives.** A proper adjective is an adjective that is made from a proper noun.
>   EXAMPLES: the Italian language, Chinese food, French tourists

B. Circle each letter that should be capitalized. Write the capital letter above it.

1. Lauren, does your friend live in miami, florida, or atlanta, georgia?

2. The potomac river forms the boundary between virginia and maryland.

3. The *pinta,* the *niña,* and the *santa maría* were the ships columbus sailed.

4. The spanish explorers discovered the mississippi river before the english settlers

   landed at jamestown.

5. The founder of the american red cross was clara barton.

6. Glaciers are found in the rocky mountains, the andes mountains, and the alps.

> - Capitalize a person's title when it comes before a name.
>   EXAMPLES: Mayor Flynn, Doctor Suarez, Governor Kuhn
> - Capitalize abbreviations of titles.
>   EXAMPLES: Ms. C. Cooke, Dr. Pearsoll, Gov. Milne, Judge Brenner

C. Circle each letter that should be capitalized. Write the capital letter above it.

1. How long have you been seeing dr. thompson?

2. Our class invited mayor thomas to speak at graduation.

3. dr. crawford w. long of Georgia is believed to be the first physician to

   use ether during surgery.

4. What time do you expect mr. and mrs. randall to arrive?

5. Most people believe senator dixon will win reelection.

6. It will be a close election unless gov. alden gives his support.

7. When is ms. howell scheduled to begin teaching?

> - Capitalize abbreviations of days and months, parts of addresses, and
>   titles of members of the armed forces. Also capitalize all letters in the
>   abbreviations of states.
>   EXAMPLES: Tues.; Nov.; 201 S. Main St.; Maj. Donna C. Plunkett;
>   Boston, MA

D. Circle each letter that should be capitalized. Write the capital letter above it.

1. niles school art fair

   sat., feb. 8th, 9 A.M.

   110 n. elm dr.

2. shoreville water festival

   june 23–24

   mirror lake

   shoreville, mn 55108

3. october fest

   october 28 and 29

   9 A.M.–5 P.M.

   63 maple st.

4. barbara dumont

   150 telson rd.

   markham, ontario L3R 1E5

5. captain c. j. neil

   c/o *ocean star*

   p.o. box 4455

   portsmouth, nh 03801

6. dr. charles b. stevens

   elmwood memorial hospital

   1411 first street

   tucson, az 85062

Using End Punctuation

- Use a **period** at the end of a declarative sentence.
  EXAMPLE: Sunlight is essential for the growth of plants.
- Use a **question mark** at the end of an interrogative sentence.
  EXAMPLE: How much sunlight does a plant need?

A. Use a period or question mark to end each sentence below.

1. Doesn't Sandra's family now live in Missouri____

2. "Snow Time" is a well-known poem____

3. Isn't someone knocking at the door, Beth____

4. Didn't Janice ask us to meet her at 2:30 this afternoon____

5. In Yellowstone Park, we saw Morning Glory Pool, Handkerchief Pool, and Old Faithful____

6. The greatest library in ancient times was in Alexandria, Egypt____

7. Aren't the employees' checks deposited in a different bank____

8. Will Ms. Wilson start interviewing applicants at 10:00 A.M.____

9. My uncle has moved to Calgary, Alberta____

10. Corn, oats, and soybeans are grown in Iowa____

11. Isn't Alex the chairperson of our committee____

12. I've mowed the lawn, pulled the weeds, and raked the leaves____

13. Did the American Revolution begin on April 19, 1775____

14. Is El Salvador in Central America____

B. Add the correct end punctuation where needed in the paragraphs below.

Did you know that experts say dogs have been around for thousands of years____ In fact, they were the first animals to be made domestic____ The ancestors of dogs were hunters____ Wolves are related to domestic dogs____ Like wolves, dogs are social animals and prefer to travel in groups____ This is called pack behavior____

There have been many famous dogs throughout history____ Can you name any of them____ In the eleventh century, one dog, Saur, was named king of Norway____ The actual king was angry because his people had removed him from the throne, so he decided to make them subjects of the dog____ The first dog in space was a Russian dog named Laika____ Laika was aboard for the 1957 journey of *Sputnik*____ Most people have heard of Rin Tin Tin and Lassie____ These dogs became famous in movies and television____

There are several hundred breeds of dogs throughout the world____ The smallest is the Chihuahua____ A Chihuahua weighs less than two pounds____ Can you think of the largest____ A Saint Bernard or a Mastiff can weigh over 150 pounds____

> - Use a **comma** between words or groups of words that are in a series.
>   EXAMPLE: Pears, peaches, plums, and figs grow in the southern states.
> - Use a comma before a conjunction in a compound sentence.
>   EXAMPLE: The farmers planted many crops, and they will work long hours to harvest them.
> - Use a comma after a subordinate clause when it begins a sentence.
>   EXAMPLE: After we ate dinner, we went to a movie.

A. Add commas where needed in the sentences below.

1. Frank Mary and Patricia are planning a surprise party for their parents.

2. It is their parents' fiftieth wedding anniversary and the children want it to be special.

3. They have invited the people their father used to work with their mother's garden club members and long-time friends of the family.

4. Even though the children are grown and living in their own homes it will be hard to make it a surprise.

5. Mr. and Mrs. Slaughter are active friendly and involved in many things.

6. For the surprise to work everyone will have to be sure not to say anything about their plans for that day.

7. This will be especially hard for the Knudsens but they will do their best.

8. Since every Sunday the families have dinner together the Knudsens will have to become very good actors the week of the party.

> - Use a comma to set off a quotation from the rest of a sentence.
>   EXAMPLES: "I want to go with you," said Paul.
>   Paul said, "I want to go with you."

B. Add commas before or after the quotations below.

1. "We're sorry that we have to cancel our plans" said Earl.

2. Carmen said "But we've done this every week for ten years!"

3. Jeanette said "We have to leave town."

4. Ivan asked "Can't you put it off just one day?"

5. "No I'm afraid we can't" said Earl.

6. "Then we'll just start over the following week" said Carmen cheerfully.

7. Jeanette said "I bet no one else has done this."

8. "I sure hate to spoil our record" said Earl.

9. "Don't worry about it" said Ivan.

10. "Yes everything will work out" said Jeanette.

> - Use a comma to set off the name of a person who is being addressed.
>   EXAMPLE: Philip, would you like to leave now?
> - Use a comma to set off words like yes, no, well, oh, first, next, and finally at the beginning of a sentence.
>   EXAMPLE: Well, we better get going.
> - Use a comma to set off an appositive.
>   EXAMPLE: Alan, Philip's brother, is a doctor in Saint Louis.

C. Add commas where needed in the sentences below.

1. Dr. Perillo a nutritionist is an expert on proper eating.

2. "Students it's important to eat a well-balanced diet," she said.

3. "Yes but how do we know what the right foods are?" asked one student.

4. "First you need to look carefully at your eating habits," said Dr. Perillo.

5. "Yes you will keep a journal of the foods you eat," she said.

6. "Dr. Perillo what do you mean by the right servings?" asked Emilio.

7. "Okay good question," she said.

8. "A serving Emilio is a certain amount of a food," said Dr. Perillo.

9. "Dave a cross-country runner will need more calories than a less active student," explained Dr. Perillo.

10. "Class remember to eat foods from the five basic food groups," she said.

D. Add commas where needed in the paragraphs below.

Our neighbor Patrick has fruit trees on his property. "Patrick what kinds of fruit do you grow?" I asked. "Well I grow peaches apricots pears and plums" he replied. "Wow! That's quite a variety" I said. Patrick's son Jonathan helps his dad care for the trees. "Oh it's constant work and care" Jonathan said "but the delicious results are worth the effort." After harvesting the fruit Jonathan's mother Allison cans the fruit for use throughout the year. She makes preserves and she gives them as gifts for special occasions. Allison sells some of her preserves to Chris Simon the owner of a local shop. People come from all over the county to buy Allison's preserves.

Jonathan's aunt Christina grows corn tomatoes beans and squash in her garden. Each year she selects her best vegetables and enters them in the fair. She has won blue ribbons medals and certificates for her vegetables. "Oh I just like being outside. That's why I enjoy gardening" Christina said. Christina's specialty squash-and-tomato bread is one of the most delicious breads I have ever tasted.

Lesson 68

Using Quotation Marks and Apostrophes

- Use **quotation marks** to show the exact words of a speaker. Use a comma or another punctuation mark to separate the quotation from the rest of the sentence.
  - EXAMPLES: "Do you have a book on helicopters?" asked Tom.
  - James said, "It's right here."
- A quotation may be placed at the beginning or at the end of a sentence. It may also be divided within the sentence.
  - EXAMPLES: Deborah said, "There are sixty active members."
  - "Morton," asked Juanita, "have you read this magazine article?"

A. Add quotation marks and other punctuation where needed in the sentences below.

1. Dan, did you ever play football asked Tim.

2. Morris asked Why didn't you come in for an interview?

3. I have never said Laurie heard a story about a ghost.

4. Selina said Yuri thank you for the present.

5. When do we start on our trip to the mountains asked Stan.

6. Our guest said You don't know how happy I am to be in your house.

7. My sister said Kelly bought those beautiful baskets in Mexico.

8. I'm going to plant the spinach said Doris as soon as I get home.

- Use an **apostrophe** in a contraction to show where a letter or letters have been taken out.
  - EXAMPLES: Amelia **didn't** answer the phone. **I've** found my wallet.
- Use an apostrophe to form a possessive noun. Add -'s to most singular nouns. Add -' to most plural nouns. Add -'s to a few nouns that have irregular plurals.
  - EXAMPLES: A **child's** toy was in our yard. The **girls'** toys were in our yard. The **children's** toys were in our yard.

B. After each sentence below, write the word in which an apostrophe has been left out. Add the apostrophe where needed.

1. Many players uniforms are red. _____

2. That dog played with the babys shoe. _____

3. Julio isnt coming with us to the library. _____

4. Its very warm for a fall day. _____

5. The captains ship was one of the newest. _____

6. Marcia doesnt sing as well as my sister does. _____

7. Mens coats are sold in the new store. _____

Using Other Punctuation

> - Use a **hyphen** between the parts of some compound words.
>   EXAMPLE: poverty-stricken   sixty-three   two-thirds
>   part-time   able-bodied   brother-in-law
>   hard-boiled   short-term   red-hot
> - Use a hyphen to separate the syllables of a word that is carried over from one line to the next.
>   EXAMPLE: So many things were going on at once that no one could possibly guess how the play would end.

A. Add hyphens where needed in the sentences below.

1. The play was going to be in an old fashioned theater.

2. The theater was so small that there were seats for only ninety two people.

3. The vice president was played by Alan Lowe.

> - Use a **colon** after the greeting in a business letter.
>   EXAMPLES: Dear Mr. Johnson: Dear Sirs:
> - Use a colon between the hour and the minute when writing the time.
>   EXAMPLES: 1:30   6:15   11:47
> - Use a colon to introduce a list.
>   EXAMPLE: Our grocery list included the following items: chicken, milk, eggs, and broccoli.

B. Add colons where needed in the sentences below.

1. At 2 1 0 this afternoon, the meeting will start.

2. Please bring the following materials with you pencils, paper,

   erasers, and a notebook.

3. The meeting should be over by 4 3 0.

4. Those of you on the special committee should bring the following items cups,

   paper plates, forks, spoons, and napkins.

> - Use a **semicolon** between the clauses of a compound sentence that are closely related but not connected by a conjunction. Do not capitalize the word after a semicolon.
>   EXAMPLE: Hummingbirds and barn swallows migrate; most sparrows live in one place all year.

C. In the sentences below, add semicolons where needed.

1. Colleen is a clever teacher she is also an inspiring one.

2. Her lectures are interesting they are full of information.

3. She has a college degree in history world history is her specialty.

4. She begins her classes by answering questions she ends them by asking questions.

Review

A. Circle each letter that should be capitalized. Then add the correct end punctuation.

1. mr. j. c. moran owns a car dealership in chicago, illinois____

2. jesse decided to apply for a job on tuesday____

3. wow, mr. moran actually offered him a job____

4. jesse will start work in june____

5. jesse is the newest employee of moran's cars and vans____

6. didn't he get auto experience when he lived in minnesota____

7. he also got training at dunwoody technical institute____

8. jesse took some computer courses there taught by mr. ted woods and ms. jane hart____

9. jesse had only temporary jobs at highland cafe and mayfield electronics for the last two years____

10. since jesse wants to be prepared for his new job, he checked out *automobile technology and the automobile industry* from the windham library____

B. Add commas where needed in the sentences below.

1. After Jesse got the new job his family friends and neighbors gave him a party.

2. Everyone brought food drinks and even some gifts.

3. Bob Jesse's roommate and Carmen Jesse's sister bought him a briefcase.

4. His mother and father bought him a new shirt jacket and tie for his first day on the job.

5. His father congratulated him by saying "Jesse we are happy for you and we wish you the best in your new job."

6. Jesse replied "Well I'm also very excited about it and I want to thank all of you for the party and the gifts."

C. Add commas and quotation marks where needed in the sentences below.

1. How did you get so lucky Jesse? asked Mike.

2. It wasn't luck answered Jesse because I studied before I applied for this job.

3. I didn't know you could study to apply for a job said Mike laughing.

4. Mike I read an employment guide before I applied said Jesse.

5. I have never heard of an employment guide! exclaimed Mike.

6. It's a great book said Jesse.

7. Jesse I'd like to apply for a job at Moran's said Mike.

8. Jesse replied Why don't you read my guide to prepare for the interview?

D. Insert apostrophes, colons, and hyphens where needed in the sentences below.

1. Joe King, Jesse's best friend, is the one who gave Jesse the employment guide to use for his interview at Moran's.

2. Jesse didn't know important interview skills.

3. The guide offered twenty-five helpful hints.

4. The guide suggested the following: dress neatly, be on time, be polite, and be enthusiastic.

5. Jesse also used the guide's suggestions for preparing a resume listing his work experience.

6. Jesse's list contained these items: his employers' names and addresses, dates of employment, and job descriptions.

7. The guide said Jesse should be a well-informed applicant, so he researched salesperson's duties and made a list of questions to ask.

8. Jesse's guide recommended getting to the interview early to have time to fill out the employer's application forms.

9. Jesse arrived at Mr. Moran's office at 3:45 for his 4:00 interview.

10. The interview lasted forty-five minutes, and Jesse was relaxed and self-confident when he left.

11. Mr. Moran's phone call the next day at 1:30 let Jesse know he had gotten the job.

12. Jesse needed to do the following: pick up a salesperson's manual, fill out employment forms, and enroll in the company's insurance program.

E. Punctuate the letter below. Circle each letter that should be capitalized.

73 e. river st.

chicago, il 65067

may 30, 1994

Dear mr. moran:

I just wanted to thank you for offering me the salespersons position with your company ____ you mentioned in our interview that my duties would be the following selling cars and vans checking customers credit references and assisting customers with their paperwork ____ ive studied the automobile sales guide that you gave me and i feel that im prepared to do a terrific job for morans ____ thank you again im looking forward to starting next monday ____

sincerely,

jesse sanchez

A. Add punctuation where needed in the paragraphs below. Circle each letter that should be capitalized. Be sure to underline book titles.

have you ever heard the story called "the dog and his bone"____ there once was a dog that had a new bone____ this is a great bone said the dog to himself____ the dog decided to take a walk and carried the bone proudly in its mouth____ he went down a dirt road and over a bridge____ as he was crossing the bridge he looked down into the river____ wow said the dog look at that big bone in the water____ the dog thought to himself id rather have that bone than the one i have right now____ can you guess what happened next____ well the dog opened his mouth and dropped the bone—a foolish thing to do—into the river____ when the splash of the bone hitting the water stopped the dog looked for the bigger bone____ however he didnt see it anymore____ what he did see was his old bone sinking to the bottom of the river____

_____

there is an incredible man scott targot who lives in my town____ his nickname is the ironman____ people call him ironman targot because he has won several triathlons____ do you know what a triathlon is____ some people consider it the ultimate sports contest____ athletes have to swim for 2.4 miles ride a bike for 112 miles and run for 26.2 miles____ just one of those alone is a lot of work____ scott will train from february to august in preparation for a triathlon in hawaii____ scott says i wouldnt want to be doing anything else with my time____ each day during training he gets up at 7 0 0 loosens up for a half hour then runs from 7 3 0 to 8 3 0____ after he cools down a little he takes a 20 mile bike ride____ at the end of the ride he swims for an hour and a half____ yes i get tired he says but i usually feel refreshed after swimming____ last he lifts light weights and takes a break to do some reading____

a triathlon is supposed to be completed in less than seventeen hours____ the record is less than half that time____ thats my goal says scott____ hes still trying to break 14 hours and ten minutes____ scotts usually one of the top finishers____

B. Rewrite the story below. Be sure to use capital letters and punctuation marks where they are needed.

sir walter scott one of the worlds greatest storytellers was born in edinburgh, scotland, on august 15, 1771____ walter had an illness just before he was two years old that left him lame for the rest of his life____ his par ents were worried so they sent him to his grandparents farm in sandy knowe____ they thought the country air would do him good____

walters parents were right____ he was quite healthy by the time he was six years old____ he was happy, too____ walter loved listening to his grandfather tell stories about scotland____ the stories stirred his imagination____ he began to read fairy tales travel books and history books____ it was these ear ly stories that laid the groundwork for Scotts later interest in writing stories____ his most famous book *Ivanhoe* has been read by people around the world____

_____

_____

_____

_____

_____

_____

_____

_____

_____

_____

_____

_____

_____

_____

Unit 4, Capitalization and Punctuation

Writing Sentences

- Every sentence has a base consisting of a simple subject and a simple predicate.
  EXAMPLE: <u>Dolphins</u> <u>leap</u>.
- Expand the meaning of a sentence by adding adjectives, adverbs, and prepositional phrases to the sentence base.
  EXAMPLE: **The sleek** dolphins **suddenly** leap **high into the air.**

A. Expand the meaning of each sentence base by adding adjectives, adverbs, and/or prepositional phrases. Write each expanded sentence.

1. (Dinner cooks.) _____

2. (Clown chuckled.) _____

3. (Car raced.) _____

4. (Dancer spun.) _____

5. (Panthers growled.) _____

6. (Leaves fall.) _____

7. (Bread baked.) _____

8. (Lake glistened.) _____

9. (Ship glides.) _____

B. Write five sentence bases. Then write an expanded sentence containing each sentence base.

1. _____

_____

2. _____

_____

3. _____

_____

4. _____

_____

5. _____

_____

> ■ A **topic sentence** is the sentence within a paragraph that states the main idea. It is often placed at the beginning of a paragraph.
>
> EXAMPLE:
>
> **The trip to the national park was a great success.** First, the visitors learned a lot from their guide about the park. They learned that the forest was created by people, not by nature. To their surprise, they found out that the park had more than five hundred species of plants. Then they went on a hike and even spotted a falcon flying overhead. Finally, the visitors had a wonderful picnic lunch and headed back home.

A. Write a topic sentence for each paragraph below.

1. Some jewelry is made out of feathers, leather, shells, or wood. Other jewelry is crafted from gold, silver, brass, copper, or other metals. Gems and unusual stones are added for their beauty and value.

Topic Sentence: _____

2. A pet goldfish needs clean water. A pump should be placed in the water to supply fresh air. The water temperature must be constant, and it must not go below 27°C (80°F). The goldfish should be fed flaked fish food or small insects.

Topic Sentence: _____

3. When Jana crawls over to a kitchen cabinet, she whips the door open to see what's behind it. With a little help from Jana, the pots and pans are on the floor in no time. If she sees a bag of groceries, Jana has to investigate the contents. After she is tucked in bed for the night, this toddler loves to climb out of her crib and explore.

Topic Sentence: _____

B. Write a topic sentence for each of the paragraph ideas below.

1. birthday parties _____

2. a great adventure _____

3. a great president _____

4. a favorite holiday _____

5. homework _____

6. video games _____

7. vacations _____

8. the Olympics _____

Writing Supporting Details

> ■ The idea expressed in a topic sentence can be developed with sentences containing **supporting details.** Details can include facts, examples, and reasons.

A. Circle the topic sentence, and underline four supporting details in the paragraph below.

In almost every professional sport, there are far more applicants than available jobs. Consider professional football. Every season, several hundred players are selected by twenty-eight professional football teams. Of those chosen, only about ten percent are actually signed by a professional team. Furthermore, this number shrinks each year because team owners want smaller and smaller teams.

B. Answer the following questions about the supporting details you underlined.

1. What is one supporting detail that is a fact?

_____

_____

_____

_____

2. What is a supporting detail that is a reason?

_____

_____

C. Read each topic sentence below, and write three supporting details for each.

1. People who want a career in sports could teach physical education.

_____

_____

_____

2. Professional sports teams employ people other than players.

_____

_____

_____

_____

> ■ One way to organize information in a paragraph is to put it in
> **chronological order**—the time in which events occurred. Words such
> as <u>first</u>, <u>next</u>, <u>second</u>, <u>then</u>, <u>finally</u>, and <u>later</u> are used to indicate the
> order in which events happen.   EXAMPLE: **First,** Mario checked his
>   tape recorder. **Then** he left for the interview.
> ■ Another way to organize information is to use **spatial order**. Words such
> as <u>above</u>, <u>near</u>, <u>over</u>, <u>beside</u>, <u>right</u>, <u>left</u>, <u>closer</u>, <u>farther</u>, <u>up</u>, and <u>down</u>
> are used to express spatial relationships.   EXAMPLE: The bald eagle sat
> on **top** of the tree. He watched the pond **below.**

A. Read each paragraph below and tell whether it is in chronological order or spatial order. For the paragraph in chronological order, underline the time order words. For the paragraph in spatial order, underline the words that indicate spatial order.

1. The park board of directors must first approve the architect's design for the

    recreation center. Then they must develop and approve a budget for the construction

    of the center. Finally, they can give approval to construction of the center.

    Order: _____

2. The plan for the recreation center includes play areas for young children. A slide

    and swingset will be built next to a large sand box. A jungle gym will be to the left

    of the slide. Children will be able to climb to the top of the jungle gym and then

    jump down to the ground.

    Order: _____

B. Number the details below in chronological order.

_____ Then early in March, the park board of directors approved the architect's design.

_____ Next, the budget was approved in April.

_____ The center's roof was finally completed in August.

_____ In January, the architect first finished his design.

C. Choose one of the scenes below. Write a paragraph of at least four sentences describing the scene. Use spatial order words to show location.

   Scenes: your house, a ballpark, a restaurant, a theater, a friend's house

_____

_____

_____

_____

Lesson 74 — Topic and Audience

- The **topic** of a story or an article is the subject written about.
- The **audience** is the group of readers.
  EXAMPLES: students, family members, neighbors, readers of a newspaper

A. Choose the most likely audience for each topic listed below.

   a. first-graders   **b.** the city council   **c.** high-school students   **d.** parents

_____ 1. Star Athlete Visits Students at Recreation Center

_____ 2. Study Shows Connection between Time Spent Exercising and Student Progress in School

_____ 3. Peter Rabbit Here for Hop and Jump Exercises

_____ 4. Council Considers Tax Plans to Finance Recreation Center

_____ 5. Tryouts for High School Track Team on Friday

_____ 6. Study Shows City Budget Shortfall Next Year

_____ 7. Kelsey School Parents' Night Next Thursday

_____ 8. Officer Safety to Visit Young Students Next Week

_____ 9. State University Considers Raising Tuition

_____ 10. Governor Approves Funds to Expand City Bus Service

B. Read the paragraph below. Then answer the questions that follow.

On Tuesday evening, May 2, 1994, at 6:00, Hawkeye, the mascot of the Child Protection Foundation, will be at the park with his handler, Officer Roy Meyers. While Hawkeye, the long-eared hound, entertains the youngsters, Officer Meyers will discuss the topic "Keeping Your Children Safe." This unusual pair has traveled across the state to introduce the findings on topics such as accidents in the home, hazardous toys, and bike safety.

1. What is the topic of the paragraph?

_____

2. Name two possible audiences for the paragraph.

_____

3. Explain why each audience might be interested.

   Audience 1: _____

   Audience 2: _____

C. Choose a topic in which you are interested. Write the name of the topic, and name the audience it would be most likely to interest.

   Topic: _____

   Audience: _____

■ A **clustering diagram** shows how ideas relate to a particular topic. The topic is written in the center. Related ideas are written around the topic. Lines show the connections between the ideas.

EXAMPLE:

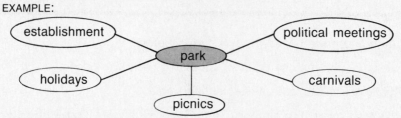

Topic Sentence: The recreation center will be built on land that was once a park.

A. Read each paragraph below. Notice the underlined topic sentence as you read. Then fill in each cluster to show how the details relating to that topic sentence could have been chosen.

1. <u>Mario had a great deal of work to do for the article.</u> He had to finish the interviews, decide what information to use, and write a rough draft. He then had to revise the draft, type the final copy, and proofread it.

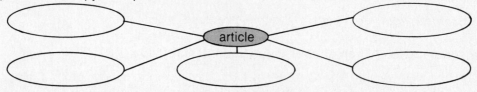

2. <u>Theresa worked hard on the article.</u> She typed the interviews. She edited the article. She organized the rough draft. Finally, she helped with the final revision and proofreading.

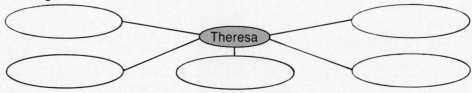

B. Rewrite the topic sentence you wrote on page 93, Exercise C.

Topic Sentence: _____

C. Write that topic from Exercise B in the center of the cluster below. Then fill in the cluster with details that would support your main topic.

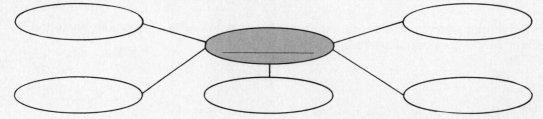

Lesson 76 — Outlining

- Before you write, organize your thoughts by making an **outline.** An outline consists of the title of the topic, headings for the main ideas, and subheadings for the supporting details.
- Main headings are listed after Roman numerals. Subheadings are listed after capital letters. Details are listed after Arabic numerals.

EXAMPLE:

Topic	Should Young People Be Paid for Doing Chores?
Main heading	I. Benefits to parents
Subheadings	A. Chores get done
	B. More leisure time
Main heading	II. Benefits to young people
Subheading	A. Learn useful skills
Details	1. Clean and do laundry
	2. Budget time
Subheading	B. Become responsible

- **Choose a topic that interests you. Then write an outline for that topic, using the example outline as a guide.**

_____

_____

_____

_____

_____

_____

_____

_____

_____

_____

_____

_____

_____

_____

_____

Persuasive Composition

■ The writer of a **persuasive composition** tries to convince others to accept a personal opinion.

A. Read the following persuasive composition.

Everyone Should Learn to Use a Computer

Knowing how to use a computer is an essential skill for everyone who wants to succeed in today's world. One basic computer program that everyone should learn to use is the word processing program. Most types of writing are easily and professionally produced with a word processing program. For example, everyone must occasionally write a business letter. Using a computer allows you to arrange and rearrange information easily, making your writing more clear and accurate. Word processing programs can help you check your spelling and grammar. A computer makes it easy to correct mistakes.

Computers can be used for much more than word processing, however. Other areas of interest and opportunity in the field of computers are graphic design, programming, and creating new games. Jobs in the computer field are growing, and strong computer skills can serve you well now and into the future.

B. Answer the questions below.

1. List three facts the writer includes to persuade the reader.

_____

_____

_____

_____

_____

_____

2. List two reasons the writer includes in the composition.

_____

_____

_____

3. List one example the writer uses to support the topic.

_____

_____

_____

C. Choose one of the topic sentences below. Write a short paragraph in which you use facts to persuade your audience about the topic.

1. The driver and front-seat passenger in a car face various consequences if they don't wear seat belts.

2. More people should car-pool or use public transportation.

_____

_____

_____

_____

_____

_____

D. Choose one of the topic sentences below. Write a short paragraph in which you use reasons to persuade your audience about the topic.

1. Wearing seat belts ensures all passengers of a safer ride.

2. The most important subject a person can learn about is _____ .

_____

_____

_____

_____

_____

_____

E. Choose one of the topic sentences below. Write a short paragraph in which you use an example to persuade your audience about the topic.

1. I know someone who wore a seat belt and survived a serious collision.

2. _____ make the best pets.

_____

_____

_____

_____

_____

_____

Revising and Proofreading

- **Revising** gives you a chance to rethink and review what you have written and to improve your writing. Revise by adding words and information, by taking out unneeded words and information, and by moving words, sentences, and paragraphs around.
- **Proofreading** has to do with checking spelling, punctuation, grammar, and capitalization. Use proofreader's marks to show changes needed in your writing.

Proofreader's Marks

≡
Capitalize.

⊙
Add a period.

ⓢ🅟
Correct spelling.

/
Make a small letter.

∧
Add something.

⊬
Indent for new paragraph.

∧
Add a comma.

⌒
Take something out.

⟶
Move something.

A. Rewrite the paragraph below. Correct the errors by following the proofreader's marks.

⊬ yellowstone national park is the oldest and largest park national in the united states. It is located partly in northwestern wyoming, partly in southern montana, and partley in easturn idaho idaho. during the summur of 1988 large parts of park the were damaged by fire. A serious lack of rein was part of the reason the fire was sew severe, one fire threatened almost to destroy the park's famous lodge, which is constructed entirely of wood. fortunately, firefighters' efforts saved the lodge from desturction. today, the forests are slowly recovering from the fires.

B. Read the paragraphs below. Use proofreader's marks to revise and proofread the paragraphs. Then write your revised paragraphs below.

although yellowstons national park is the largest national national park in the United states, other national parks are also well-known yosemite national park in california has acres of Mountain Scenery and miles of hiking trails. Won of the world's largest biggest waterfalls can also be found in yosemite.

mammoth cave national park in kentucky features a huge underground cave the cave over has 212 miles of corridors it also have underground lakes rivers and waterfalls this cave system is estimated to be millions of years old

many pepul are surprized to learn that their are national parks in alaska and hawaii. mount McKinley the highest mountain in north america is located in denali national park in alaska. you can travel to hawaii and visit hawaii volcanoes national park this Park Has too active volcanoes rare plants and animals.

_____

_____

_____

_____

_____

_____

_____

_____

_____

_____

_____

_____

_____

_____

_____

A. Expand the sentence bases below by adding adjectives, adverbs, and prepositional phrases.

   1. (Friends visited.)

   _____

   2. (Actors prepared.)

   _____

   3. (Window broke.)

   _____

B. Read the paragraph below. Then circle the topic sentence, and underline only the supporting details.

       Phonograph records have changed over the years. Thomas Edison made them from glass, and he used sound waves to carve the grooves into the records. Edison also invented electricity. Later, phonographic records were made of plastic. Today's compact discs are made of aluminum.

C. Complete the cluster for the topic given in the center.

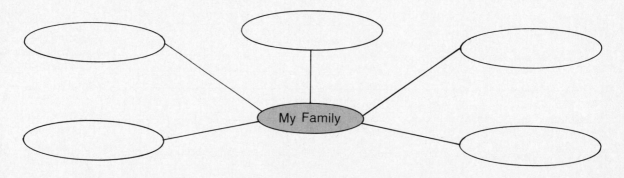

D. Begin an outline based on that cluster.

   Topic: My Family

   I. _____

      A. _____

      B. _____

  II. _____

      A. _____

      B. _____

E. Write the items in outline form.

Topic: Pruning trees takes great skill.
Rake tree trash
Climb the tree
Choose and trim bad wood

Cleaning up
Haul trash
Brace your body firmly
Pruning the tree

_____

_____

_____

_____

_____

_____

_____

F. Read the persuasive paragraph. Then answer the questions below.

Everyone Should Vote

Elections are important, no matter what they are for. Voting in an election is democracy in action. Unless you take advantage of this privilege, you are letting a few people make your decisions for you. These decisions may be as small as who becomes class president or as important as who becomes the leader of an entire nation. Exercise your rights and make your beliefs and wishes known—vote in every election you possibly can.

1. What is one reason the writer gives for everyone to vote?

_____

2. What is one example the writer gives for the importance of voting?

_____

G. Read the paragraph below. Use proofreader's marks to revise and proofread the paragraph. Then write your revised paragraph below.

Artists choose from his materials that already are in existents to create their works of art all materials have there

own qualities. artists must know the characteristicks of their chosen materyal. They must work with it and not

aginst it materials are shaped in many ways cutting melting, hammering, and wearving are some of those waze.

_____

_____

_____

_____

A. Choose one of the topic sentences below. Write a short paragraph in which you use facts to persuade your audience about the topic.

1. Certain rules that apply to children do not apply to adults.
2. Community recycling programs benefit the environment.
3. A regular fitness program has many benefits.

_____

_____

_____

_____

_____

B. Choose one of the topic sentences below. Write a short paragraph in which you use reasons to persuade your audience about the topic.

1. Being a teacher is one of the most important jobs a person can have.
2. It is important to protect endangered animals from extinction.
3. High-school students should be required to take a driver-education course.

_____

_____

_____

_____

_____

C. Choose one of the topic sentences below. Write a short paragraph in which you use an example to persuade your audience about the topic.

1. Dogs can be trained to be more than just pets.
2. A high-school diploma is necessary for obtaining many jobs.
3. You can learn a great deal about life from books.

_____

_____

_____

_____

_____

D. Choose another topic from Exercises A, B, or C. Write a statement for a composition in which you wish to persuade your audience to consider your idea about the topic.

_____

E. Write a short outline of your ideas. Include main headings, subheadings, and details.

_____

_____

_____

_____

_____

_____

_____

_____

_____

F. Write the first and second paragraphs of a short composition that persuades people about your idea. Use the outline you wrote as a guide. Then revise your paragraphs, and proofread them.

_____

_____

_____

_____

_____

_____

_____

_____

_____

_____

_____

Dictionary: Guide Words

- A **dictionary** is a reference book that contains definitions of words and other information about their history and use.
- **Entries** in a dictionary are listed in **alphabetical order.**
- **Guide words** appear at the top of each dictionary page. Guide words show the first and last entry on the page.
  EXAMPLE: The word <u>dog</u> would appear on a dictionary page with the guide words <u>dodge</u> / <u>doll</u>. The word <u>dull</u> would not.

A. Put a check in front of each word that would be listed on the dictionary page with the given guide words.

1. frozen / gather

_____ fruit

_____ grain

_____ furnish

_____ gate

_____ gallon

_____ former

_____ forgive

_____ fuzz

_____ galaxy

_____ future

2. money / muscle

_____ muddy

_____ moss

_____ motorcycle

_____ mustard

_____ moisten

_____ moose

_____ museum

_____ morning

_____ mortal

_____ modest

3. perfect / pin

_____ perfume

_____ pit

_____ pick

_____ photo

_____ pest

_____ plastic

_____ pillow

_____ pile

_____ pipe

_____ pizza

B. Number the words in each column in the order in which they would appear in a dictionary. Then write the words that could be the guide words for each column.

1. _____ / _____

_____ raccoon

_____ radar

_____ rabbit

_____ raisin

_____ react

_____ reflect

_____ rebel

_____ rainfall

_____ relay

_____ remind

_____ refuse

_____ ran

2. _____ / _____

_____ seize

_____ shellfish

_____ shrink

_____ signal

_____ silent

_____ scent

_____ shuffle

_____ shaft

_____ serpent

_____ seldom

_____ scope

_____ selfish

3. _____ / _____

_____ octopus

_____ olive

_____ of

_____ office

_____ old

_____ odor

_____ once

_____ oil

_____ odd

_____ onion

_____ occasion

_____ only

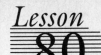

Dictionary: Syllables

> ■ A **syllable** is a part of a word that is pronounced at one time. Dictionary entry words are divided into syllables to show how they can be divided at the end of a writing line.
> ■ A **hyphen** (-) is placed between syllables to separate them.
> EXAMPLE: quar-ter-back
> ■ If a word has a beginning or ending syllable of only one letter, do not divide it so that one letter stands alone.
> EXAMPLES: a-fraid   bus-y

A. Find each word in a dictionary. Then write each word with a hyphen between each syllable.

1. allowance _____

2. porridge _____

3. harness _____

4. peddle _____

5. character _____

6. hickory _____

7. solution _____

8. variety _____

9. talent _____

10. weather _____

11. brilliant _____

12. enthusiasm _____

13. dramatic _____

14. employment _____

15. laboratory _____

16. judgment _____

17. kingdom _____

18. recognize _____

19. usual _____

20. yesterday _____

B. Write two ways in which each word may be divided at the end of a writing line.

1. victorious   vic-torious   victori-ous

2. inferior _____ _____

3. quantity _____ _____

4. satisfactory _____ _____

5. security _____ _____

6. possession _____ _____

7. thermometer _____ _____

8. getaway _____ _____

Dictionary: Pronunciation

- Each dictionary entry word is followed by a respelling that shows how the word is **pronounced**.
- **Accent marks** (′) show which syllable or syllables are said with extra stress. A syllable pronounced with more stress than the others receives primary stress, shown by a heavy accent mark (′). A syllable said with lighter force receives secondary stress, shown by a lighter accent mark (′).
  EXAMPLE: con-grat-u-late (kən grach′ ə lāt′)
- A **pronunciation key** (shown below) explains the other symbols used in the respellings.

A. Use the pronunciation key to answer the questions.

1. Which word tells you how to pronounce the e in knee?

   _____

2. How many words are given for the symbol ə?

   _____

3. What symbol is used for the sound of the s in treasure?

   _____

4. What symbol would be used for the sound of o in rob? _____

5. What symbol would be used for the sound of a in mark? _____

at; āpe; fär; câre; end; mē; it; īce; pîerce; hot; ōld; sông; fôrk; oil; out; up; ūse; rüle; pu̇ll; tûrn; chin; sing; shop; thin; this; hw in white; zh in treasure. The symbol ə stands for the unstressed vowel sound in about, taken, pencil, lemon, and circus.

B. Use the pronunciation key to help you choose the correct word for each respelling. Underline the correct word.

1. (ōn)   own   an   on
2. (hēt)   heat   height   hate
3. (rod)   rode   road   rod
4. (tôk)   take   talk   took
5. (spēd)   speed   sped   spade
6. (wô′ tər) waiter   whiter   water
7. (wāt)   wait   what   white
8. (spel)   spill   spoil   spell
9. (ān′ jəl) angry   angel   angle
10. (must)   mist   must   most
11. (fēr)   fear   far   fir
12. (härd)   herd   hard   hoard
13. (frīt)   freight   fruit   fright
14. (sün)   sun   soon   sound

Dictionary: Definitions and Parts of Speech

> - A dictionary lists the **definitions** of each entry word. Many words have more than one definition. In this case, the most commonly used definition is given first. Sometimes a definition is followed by a sentence showing a use of the entry word.
> - A dictionary also tells the **part of speech** for each entry word. An abbreviation (shown below) stands for each part of speech. Some words may be used as more than one part of speech.
>   EXAMPLE: **need** (nēd) *n.* **1.** the lack of something wanted or necessary. **2.** something wanted or necessary: *What are your basic needs for the camping trip?* *-v.* to require.

- **Use the dictionary samples below to answer the questions.**

pop-u-lar (pop′ yə lər) *adj.* **1.** pleasing to many people. **2.** having many friends: *Angela was voted the most popular girl in her class.* **3.** accepted by the general public: *The idea that pencils contain lead is a popular error.*

por-poise (pôr′ pəs) *n.* a warm-blooded marine mammal that is related to the dolphin.

por-tion (pôr′ shən) *n.* **1.** a part of a whole: *We spent a portion of the day at the park.* **2.** a part or share of a whole belonging to a person or a group. **3.** a helping of food served to one person. *-v.* to divide into parts or shares.

por-tray (pôr trā′) *v.* **1.** to draw or paint a picture of: *The artist portrayed the beautiful mountains in a painting.* **2.** to give a picture of in words; describe.

1. Which word can be used as either a noun

   or a verb? _____

2. Which entry word has the most example

   sentences? _____

3. What part of speech is <u>porpoise</u>?

   _____

n.	noun
pron.	pronoun
v.	verb
adj.	adjective
adv.	adverb
prep.	preposition

4. How many definitions are given for the word <u>porpoise</u>? _____

   for <u>portion</u>? _____   for <u>portray</u>? _____

5. Write the most commonly used definition of <u>popular</u>. _____

   _____

6. Use the first definition of <u>popular</u> in a sentence. _____

   _____

7. Write a sentence in which you use <u>portion</u> as a verb. _____

   _____

8. Use the second definition of <u>portray</u> in a sentence. _____

   _____

> ■ An **etymology** is the origin and development of a word. Many dictionary entries include etymologies. The etymology is usually enclosed in brackets [ ].
>
> EXAMPLE: **knit** [ME *knitten* < OE *cnyttan*, to knot]. The word *knit* comes from the Middle English word *knitten*, which came from the Old English word *cnyttan*, meaning "to tie in a knot."

■ **Use these dictionary entries to answer the questions.**

cam-pus (kam′ pəs) *n.* the grounds and buildings of a school or university. [Latin *campus*, meaning field, perhaps because most colleges used to be in the country.]

chaise longue (shāz lông′) *n.* a chair with a long seat which supports the sitter's outstretched legs. [French *chaise*, chair + *longue*, long.]

gar-de-nia (gär dēn′ yə) *n.* a fragrant yellow or white flower from an evergreen shrub or tree. [Modern Latin *Gardenia*, from Alexander *Garden*, 1730–1791, U.S. scientist who studied plants.]

pas-teur-ize (pas′ chə rīz) *v.* to heat food to a high temperature in order to destroy harmful bacteria. [From Louis *Pasteur*, inventor of the process.]

rent (rent) *n.* a regular payment for the use of property. [Old French *rente*, meaning taxes.]

ut-ter (ut′ ər) *v.* to express; make known; put forth. [From Middle English or Dutch, *utteren*, literally, out.]

wam-pum (wom′ pəm) *n.* small beads made from shells and used for money or jewelry. [Short for Algonquin *wampompeag*, meaning strings of money.]

1. Which word comes from an Algonquin word? _____

2. What does the Algonquin word mean? _____

3. Which word was formed from the name of an inventor? _____

4. Which word comes from French words? _____

5. What do the French words chaise and longue mean? _____

6. Which word was formed from the name of a scientist? _____

7. Which word is short for the word wampompeag? _____

8. Which words come from Latin words? _____

9. Which word comes from a Middle English word? _____

10. What does the French word rente mean? _____

11. Which word comes from two languages? _____

12. What does the word utteren mean? _____

13. What does the Latin word campus mean? _____

14. Which word is the name of a flower? _____

15. Which word names a piece of furniture? _____

Using Parts of a Book

> - A **title page** lists the name of a book and its author.
> - A **copyright page** tells who published the book, where it was published, and when it was published.
> - A **table of contents** lists the chapter or unit titles and the page numbers on which they begin. It is at the front of a book.
> - An **index** gives a detailed list of the topics in a book and the page numbers on which each topic is found. It is in the back of a book.

A. Answer the questions below.

1. Where should you look for the page number of a particular topic? _____

2. Where should you look to find out who wrote a book? _____

3. Where should you look to get a general idea of the contents of a book? _____

4. Where should you look to find out when a book was published? _____

5. Where should you look to find the name of the book? _____

6. Where should you look to find out who published a book? _____

B. Use your *Language Exercises* book to answer the questions.

1. What company published this book? _____

2. How many units are in this book? _____

3. On what page does Unit 2 start? _____

4. Where is the index located? _____

5. What is the copyright date? _____

6. What pages contain lessons on pronouns? _____

7. On what page does Unit 5 start? _____

8. On what pages are the lessons on commas found? _____

9. What lesson is on page 86? _____

10. List the pages that teach prepositions. _____

11. On what page is the lesson on guide words found? _____

12. On what page is the lesson on prefixes found? _____

13. On what page does Unit 3 start? _____

Lesson 85

Using Visual Aids

- A **chart** lists information in columns, which you read down, and rows, which you read across. The information can be either words or numbers.
- A **graph** shows how quantities change over time. It often shows how two or more things change in relation to one another. The information can be shown through the use of lines, dots, bars, pictures, or in a circle.

A. Use the chart and the graph to answer the following questions.

Library Use Chart

Day of the Week	Science Students	History Students
Monday	18	5
Tuesday	22	16
Wednesday	14	10
Thursday	4	20
Friday	13	15

Library Use Graph

Graph Key
Science students _____
History students _ _ _ _

1. How many science students used the library on Monday? _____ on Tuesday? _____

   on Wednesday? _____ on Thursday? _____ on Friday? _____

2. Can the question in number 1 be answered by studying the Library Use Chart? _____

   the Library Use Graph? _____

3. On which day was the number of science and history students using the library

   nearly the same? _____

4. On which day did the most science and history students use the library? _____

5. How many science and history students used the library on the day

   mentioned in number 4? _____

6. On which day did the least number of science and history students use the library? _____

- A **road map** is another valuable type of visual aid. Maps like the one shown below are helpful when you are unfamiliar with a certain area. To use any map, you should refer to its **legend, compass rose,** and **scale.**
- The legend tells what each symbol represents.
- The compass rose is made up of arrows that point north, south, east, and west.
- The scale allows you to determine how far it is from one location to another. To use the scale, mark the distance between any two locations along the edge of a sheet of paper. Then place the sheet of paper alongside the scale of distance, lining up one of the marks with zero. This will allow you to read the distance between the two locations.

B. Use the map to answer the questions below.

Carsonville

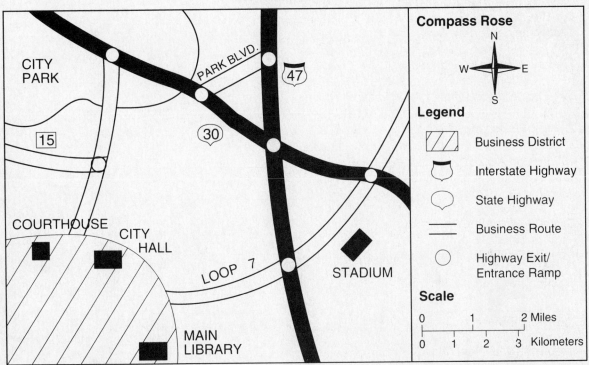

1. Which direction from the business district is City Park? _____

2. On what road is the stadium? _____

3. How many miles is it from City Hall to the Main Library? _____

4. What kind of highway is 30? _____

5. Does Business Route 15 run north/south or east/west? _____

6. Is the Courthouse within the business district? _____

7. How many exit ramps are there on Highway 30 from Loop 7 to City Park? _____

8. How many miles will you travel if you drive from City Park to the stadium? _____

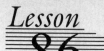
Using the Library

> ■ Books are arranged on library shelves according to **call numbers.** Each book is assigned a number from 000 to 999, according to its subject matter. The following are the main subject groups for call numbers:
>
> | | | | |
> |---|---|---|---|
> | 000–099 | Reference | 500–599 | Science and Mathematics |
> | 100–199 | Philosophy | 600–699 | Technology |
> | 200–299 | Religion | 700–799 | The Arts |
> | 300–399 | Social Sciences | 800–899 | Literature |
> | 400–499 | Languages | 900–999 | History and Geography |

A. Write the call number group in which you would find each book.

1. *Australia: The Island Continent* _____

2. *Technology in a New Age* _____

3. *French: A Romance Language* _____

4. *Solving Word Problems in Mathematics* _____

5. *Ancient Philosophy* _____

6. *1993 World Almanac and Book of Facts* _____

7. *Artists of the 1920's* _____

8. *Funny Poems for a Rainy Day* _____

9. *Science Experiments for Teen-agers* _____

10. *People in Society* _____

11. *Russian Folktales* _____

12. *Religions Around the World* _____

13. *World War I: The Complete Story* _____

14. *Encyclopaedia Britannica* _____

15. *The Social Characteristics of Pack Animals* _____

B. Write the titles of three of your favorite books. Write the call number range beside each title.

1. _____

2. _____

3. _____

Using the Card Catalog

- The **card catalog** contains information cards on every book in the library. Some libraries are now computerized and have no card catalogs. But the information in the computer is filed in the same manner as the information in the card catalog.
- Each book has three cards in the catalog. They are filed separately according to:
  1. the author's last name
  2. the subject of the book
  3. the title of the book

A. Use the sample catalog card to answer the questions.

Author Card

Call number — 920.067 H66

Author — Hoobler, Dorothy and Thomas

Title — Images across the ages: African portraits; illustrated by

John Gampert. — Austin : Raintree/Steck-Vaughn — Publisher

Place published

Date published — ©1993

Number of pages — 96 p. : illus. — Illustrated

1. What are the authors' names? _____

2. What is the title of the book? _____

3. How many pages does the book have? _____

4. What is the call number of the book? _____

5. When was the book published? _____

6. What subject might this book be filed under? _____

B. Write <u>author</u>, <u>title</u>, or <u>subject</u> to tell which card you would look for to locate the book or books.

1. books about national parks in the United States _____

2. *The Adventures of Huckleberry Finn* _____

3. a novel by Sylvia Cassidy _____

4. books about Helen Keller _____

5. a book of poems by Vachel Lindsay _____

6. *Children's Verse in America* _____

> - An **encyclopedia** is a reference book that contains articles on many different topics. The articles are arranged alphabetically in volumes. Each volume is marked to show which articles are inside.
> - Guide words are used to show the first topic on each page.
> - At the end of most articles there is a listing of **cross-references** to related topics for the reader to investigate.

A. Find the entry for <u>Knute Rockne</u> in an encyclopedia. Then answer the following questions.

1. What encyclopedia did you use? _____

2. When did Knute Rockne live? _____

3. Where was he born? _____

4. Where did he go to college? _____

5. For what is he best known? _____

B. Find the entry for <u>Redwood</u> in an encyclopedia. Then answer the following questions.

1. What encyclopedia did you use? _____

2. Where does the redwood tree grow? _____

3. By what other name is it known? _____

4. What is special about this tree? _____

5. How tall do most redwoods grow? _____

C. Find the entry in an encyclopedia for a person in whom you are interested. Then answer the following questions.

1. Who is your subject? _____

2. What encyclopedia did you use? _____

3. When did the person live? _____

4. Where did the person live? _____

5. What is it about the person that makes him or her famous? _____

_____

6. What cross-references are listed? _____

> ■ A **thesaurus** is a reference book that writers use to find the exact
> words they need. Like a dictionary, a thesaurus lists its entry words
> alphabetically. Each entry word has a list of **synonyms,** or words that
> can be used in its place. Some thesauruses also list **antonyms** for the
> entry word.
>   EXAMPLE: You have just written the following sentence:
>   The children **laughed** as the tiny puppy licked their faces.
>   With the help of a thesaurus, you could improve the sentence
>   by replacing laughed with its more precise synonym giggled.
>   The children **giggled** as the tiny puppy licked their faces.

A. Use the thesaurus sample below to answer the questions.

> **move** *v.* *syn.* turn, budge, shift, retrieve, carry, transport,
> retreat, crawl, arouse, progress. *ant.* stay, stop, stabilize

1. Which is the entry word? _____

2. What are its synonyms? _____

   _____

3. Which word would you use in place of excite? _____

4. Which word would you use in place of rotate? _____

5. What are the antonyms of move? _____

6. Which antonym would you use in place of remain? _____

B. Use the synonyms of move to complete the sentences.

1. Sharon asked me if I would _____ the groceries in from the car.

2. Spot was able to _____ the golf ball from the lake.

3. Ryan's job is to _____ fruit from Michigan to other parts of the country.

4. The surfer had to _____ his weight from one leg to the other to
   keep his balance.

5. The instructor asked the students to _____ around in their chairs so they
   could see the map.

6. A baby has to _____ in order to get around.

7. We hope to _____ steadily up the mountain by climbing from ledge to ledge.

8. Robert wouldn't _____ from his favorite spot under the kitchen table.

■ The ***Readers' Guide to Periodical Literature*** lists by author and by subject all the articles that appear in nearly two hundred magazines. Use the *Readers' Guide* when you need
  ● recent articles on a particular subject,
  ● several articles written over a period of time about the same subject,
  ● many articles written by the same author.

■ **Use the *Readers' Guide* samples to answer the questions below.**

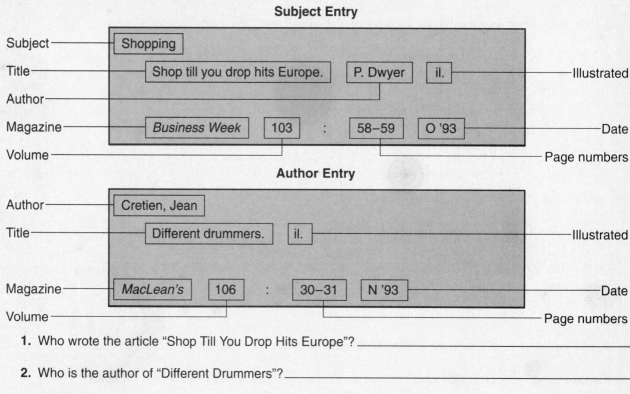

Subject Entry

Subject — Shopping
Title — Shop till you drop hits Europe. — P. Dwyer — il. — Illustrated
Author
Magazine — *Business Week* — 103 : 58–59 — O '93 — Date
Volume — Page numbers

Author Entry

Author — Cretien, Jean
Title — Different drummers. — il. — Illustrated
Magazine — *MacLean's* — 106 : 30–31 — N '93 — Date
Volume — Page numbers

1. Who wrote the article "Shop Till You Drop Hits Europe"? _____

2. Who is the author of "Different Drummers"? _____

3. In what magazine will you find the article "Shop Till You Drop Hits Europe"? _____

4. Under what subject entry can you find the article "Shop Till You Drop Hits Europe"? _____

5. In what volume of *MacLean's* does "Different Drummers" appear? _____

6. In what month and year was "Different Drummers" published? _____

7. Which article is illustrated? _____

8. In what month and year was "Shop Till You Drop Hits Europe" published? _____

9. On what pages will you find "Different Drummers"? _____

10. On what pages will you find the article "Shop Till You Drop Hits Europe"? _____

Using an Atlas

> ■ An **atlas** is a reference book that uses maps to organize pertinent facts about states, provinces, countries, continents, and bodies of water. Additional maps show information on topography; resources, industry, and agriculture; vegetation; population; and climate.

A. Use the sample atlas entry to answer the questions below.

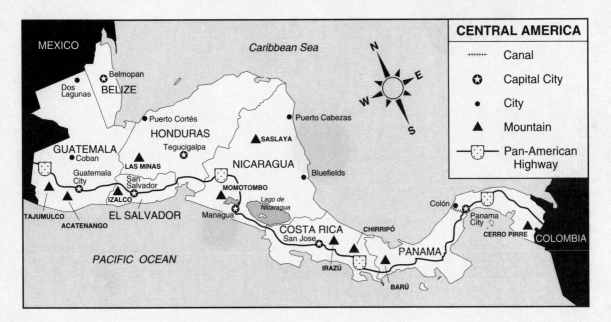

1. What part of the world is shown on this map? _____

2. How many countries make up Central America? _____

3. Which mountain is farthest west? _____

4. What major highway is shown on the map? _____

5. Which country has no mountains? _____

6. What is the capital of Nicaragua? _____

B. Answer the questions.

1. What kind of map would you use to find out where most mining occurs in a country? _____

2. Would a topographical map show you where the most people live or where the most mountains are? _____

   _____

3. What kind of map would you use to decide what clothes to pack for a July trip to Japan? _____

- An **almanac** is a reference book that presents useful information on a wide variety of topics. Much of this information is in the form of tables, charts, graphs, and time lines.

- **Use the sample almanac page to answer the questions.**

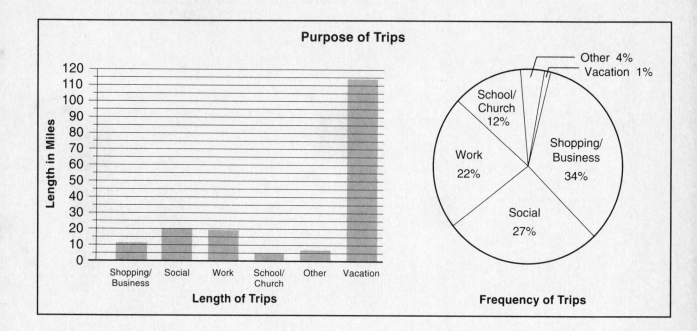

1. Which trip accounts for the most miles traveled? _____

2. What reason do most people give for taking trips? _____

3. Which three purposes together account for 60% of all trips? _____

4. Which graph shows how often people travel for a specific purpose? _____

5. Which trips are the shortest? _____

6. Do people travel farther for work or for social reasons? _____

7. Out of 100 trips, how many are made for shopping/business reasons? _____

8. What is the length of the trip least often taken? _____

9. What is the length of the trip most often taken? _____

10. Do people travel more often for school/church or for social reasons? _____

Choosing Reference Sources

- Use a **dictionary** to find the definitions of words and pronunciations of words, suggestions for word usage, and etymologies.
- Use an **encyclopedia** to find articles about many different people, places, and other subjects. Use an encyclopedia to find references to related subjects.
- Use a **thesaurus** to find synonyms and antonyms.
- Use the *Readers' Guide to Periodical Literature* to find magazine articles on specific subjects or by particular authors.
- Use an **atlas** to find maps and other information about geographical locations.
- Use an **almanac,** an annual publication, to find such information as population numbers, annual rainfall, election statistics, and other specific information for a given year.

- Write <u>dictionary</u>, <u>encyclopedia</u>, <u>thesaurus</u>, *Readers' Guide,* <u>atlas</u>, or <u>almanac</u> to show where you would find the following information. Some information may be found in more than one source.

_____ 1. the life of Queen Elizabeth I

_____ 2. an article on the latest space shuttle flight

_____ 3. the states and provinces through which the Rocky Mountains run

_____ 4. the origin of the word <u>tomato</u>

_____ 5. the annual rainfall for Somalia

_____ 6. the most direct route from California to Alberta

_____ 7. an antonym for the word <u>happy</u>

_____ 8. the meaning of the word <u>spar</u>

_____ 9. recent articles written on the subject of air pollution

_____ 10. the pronunciation of the word <u>wren</u>

_____ 11. the life of Sigmund Freud

_____ 12. a synonym for the word <u>bad</u>

_____ 13. the years during which World War I was fought

_____ 14. an article on rock climbing

_____ 15. the final standings of the National Hockey League for last year

_____ 16. the meaning of the word <u>history</u>

Using Reference Sources

■ Use reference sources—dictionaries, encyclopedias, the *Readers' Guide to Periodical Literature,* thesauruses, atlases, and almanacs—to find information about people, places, or things with which you are not familiar. You can also use these sources to learn more about subjects that interest you.

A. Follow the directions below.

1. Find the entry for your state in one of the reference sources. Write the exact title

   of the reference source. _____

2. Write a brief summary of the information you found about your state.

   _____

   _____

   _____

   _____

   _____

   _____

B. Follow the directions, and answer the questions.

1. Choose a famous person you would like to know more about.

   Person's name: _____

2. List two reference sources you can use to find information about this person.

   1. _____   2. _____

3. Use one of the sources you listed above to find out when the person was born.

   Write the date of birth. _____

4. Use the appropriate reference source to find the title of the most recent article written about the person. Write the title of the article.

   _____

5. Use either reference source you listed in number two. Find the entry for the person you are researching. Write a short summary of the information you found.

   _____

   _____

   _____

C. Follow the directions, and answer the questions.

1. Choose a country you would like to know more about.

   Name of country: _____

2. List four reference sources that you can use to find information about this country.

   a. _____   c. _____

   b. _____   d. _____

3. Find the entry for the country in one of the reference sources you listed.
   Write the exact title of the reference source.

   _____

4. Write a short summary of the information you found.

   _____

   _____

   _____

   _____

   _____

5. Find the entry for the country in one other reference source. Write the exact
   title of the reference source.

   _____

6. What new information did you find about the country?

   _____

   _____

   _____

D. Follow the directions, and answer the questions below.

1. In what state do you live? _____

2. Find the entry for your state in one of the reference sources. Write the exact

   title of the reference source. _____

3. Write a short summary of the information you found about your state.

   _____

   _____

   _____

   _____

A. Use the dictionary samples to answer the questions below.

tux-e-do (tuk sē′ dō) *n.* a man's formal suit, usually black, having a jacket with satin lapels and trousers with a stripe of satin along the outer side of each leg. [From *Tuxedo Park, New York*, an exclusive community where this suit was popular during the nineteenth century.]

twin (twin) *n.* **1.** one of two offspring born at the same birth. **2.** either of two people, animals, or things that are very much or exactly alike. *-adj.* **1.** being one of two born as twins. **2.** being one of two things that are very much or exactly alike: *The fort had twin towers. -v.* to give birth to twins.

1. What part of speech is tuxedo? _____

2. How many definitions are given for tuxedo? _____

3. How many definitions are given for the noun twin? _____

4. Which word can be used as an adjective? _____

5. Which word comes from the name of a place in New York? _____

6. How many syllables are there in tuxedo? _____

   in twin? _____

7. What parts of speech is twin? _____

8. Underline the pair of words that could be guide words for the dictionary entries above.

   a. turtle / twill   **c.** tusk / twirl

   b. twang / twist   **d.** Tuscan / twig

n.	noun
pron.	pronoun
v.	verb
adj.	adjective
adv.	adverb
prep.	preposition

B. Write the part of the book you would use to answer the following questions.

1. What is the name of Chapter 2? _____

2. Who wrote the book? _____

3. When was the book published? _____

4. Does the book have information on Martin Luther King, Jr.? _____

C. Write the answers to the questions below.

1. How are books arranged on library shelves? _____

2. What are the three types of cards each book has in a card catalog? _____

   _____

3. Which type of card would you use to locate a book by Ansel Adams? _____

D. Use the map to answer the questions.

Franklin Point

1. Which direction is the city from the park? _____

2. What kind of highway is 37? _____

3. How far is it from the exit on River Road to the golf course? _____

E. Use the sample thesaurus entry below to answer the questions.

> **activity** *n.* **syn.** action, movement, motion
> **ant.** inactivity, inaction, motionlessness

1. What is the entry word? _____

2. What are its antonyms? _____

F. Use the *Readers' Guide* sample to answer the questions.

> **KAGARLITSKY, BORIS**
> Make Them Truly Democratic. The Nation 257:688–702 Dec '93

1. What is the title of the article? _____

2. In what magazine does the article appear? _____

3. On what pages will you find the article? _____

G. Write dictionary, encyclopedia, thesaurus, *Readers' Guide*, atlas, or almanac to show where you would find the following information.

1. the most direct route from Calgary, Alberta, to Albuquerque, New Mexico _____

2. the pronunciation of the word sedentary _____

3. an antonym for the word bright _____

4. the life of John James Audubon _____

5. the increase in world population last year _____

A. Find the word humor in your dictionary. Then follow the directions and answer the questions.

1. Write the guide words from the page on which you found the entry for humor. _____

2. Write humor in syllables. _____

3. As what parts of speech can humor be used? _____

4. Write the history of the word. _____

_____

B. Use the sample catalog card to answer the questions.

> 520.0
>
> **Lambert, David**
>   Stars and planets: includes information on the planets, the solar system, astronomy, and astronautics in astronomy.
> Austin, Texas, Colonial Press [1994]   32 p.   illus.

1. What type of catalog card is this?

   a. subject card   **b.** author card   **c.** title card

2. What is the call number of the book? _____

3. What is the title of the book? _____

4. Is the book illustrated? _____

C. Use the encyclopedia sample to answer the questions.

> **CREE** is the name of a Native American people now living on reservations in Canada. They were originally forest hunters and trappers who traded with the early French and English fur traders. Part of the group moved southwest into buffalo country and became known as Plaines Cree. *See also* NATIVE AMERICANS.

1. What is the article about? _____

2. Where did some members of the tribe move? _____

3. Under what subject heading can you find related information?

_____

D. Use the *Readers' Guide* sample to answer the questions.

> **HERTSGAARD, MARK**
> Onward and Upward with the Arts: Letting It Be.
> il New Yorker 69: Jan 24, '94

1. What is the title of the article? _____

2. Who is the author? _____

3. In what magazine does the article appear? _____

E. Use a thesaurus to find a synonym for each underlined word.

_____ 1. My milk shake was so large that I couldn't finish it.

_____ 2. The police found our stolen property.

F. Use the information in the chart to complete the graph. Then answer the questions.

Club Membership

Chart

Year	Men	Women
1960	40	40
1970	30	10
1980	20	30
1990	30	30

Graph

Total Number of Members (y-axis: 0, 10, 20, 30, 40, 50, 60)
Years (x-axis: 1960, 1970, 1980, 1990)

> **Graph Key**
> Men _____
> Women _ _ _ _ _ _ _ _ _

1. How many women belonged to the club in 1960? _____

2. What was the total number of members in 1960? _____

3. What two years had an equal number of members? _____

G. Use the sample encyclopedia index entry to answer the questions.

> **Generation(s),** 5-877; *See also* Families; Grandparents

1. In what volume is the article on generations? _____

2. On what page does the article begin? _____

Synonyms and Antonyms ▪ On the line before each pair of words, write <u>S</u> if they are synonyms, or <u>A</u> if they are antonyms.

_____ 1. brave, courageous   _____ 4. late, early   _____ 7. begin, end

_____ 2. start, commence   _____ 5. smile, grin   _____ 8. country, nation

_____ 3. happy, unhappy   _____ 6. quick, slow   _____ 9. sweet, sour

Homonyms ▪ Underline the correct homonyms in each sentence below.

1. Tina went (by, buy)(plain, plane) to visit her (ant, aunt).

2. We had a (great, grate) tour of the (capital, capitol) building.

3. The kitten had white (hair, hare), large (pause, paws), and a long (tail, tale).

Homographs ▪ Circle the letter for the best definition for each underlined homograph.

1. Lee ate the <u>rest</u> of the meatball sandwich.

   a. part left over   **b.** inactive period of time

2. The heat in the <u>desert</u> was unbearable.

   a. to abandon   **b.** dry, barren land

3. John's <u>club</u> had a car wash to raise money for their trip.

   a. a heavy wooden stick   **b.** an organization of people

4. The room is <u>light</u> because it has many windows.

   a. bright   **b.** not heavy

5. Please <u>tear</u> the article out of the magazine for me.

   a. a drop of water from the eye   **b.** rip

Prefixes, Suffixes, and Compound Words ▪ Write <u>P</u> if the underlined word has a prefix, write <u>S</u> if it has a suffix, and write <u>C</u> if it is a compound word.

1. _____ _____ Tony was <u>careful</u> as he walked <u>uphill</u> to the soggy field.

2. _____ _____ It seemed awfully wet for the <u>softball</u> game. He was not <u>hopeful</u>.

3. _____ _____ He began to <u>rethink</u> his decision to play. Perhaps he had been <u>foolish</u>.

4. _____ _____ His <u>teammates</u> would be <u>helpless</u> in this mud.

5. _____ _____ The other team felt <u>unhappy</u>. They said running could be <u>hazardous</u>.

6. _____ _____ Suddenly there was a <u>downpour</u>. They would be <u>unable</u> to play.

7. _____ _____ They decided to <u>reschedule</u> the game for the next Thursday <u>afternoon</u>.

8. _____ _____ Tony's team was <u>thankful</u> for the delay. They needed the <u>weekend</u> for extra practice.

9. _____ _____ The game is an important one for <u>everyone</u>. Neither team's <u>pitcher</u> has lost a game yet.

Contractions ▪ Write the contraction for each pair of words.

1. I am _____

2. would not _____

3. do not _____

4. I have _____

5. you have _____

6. is not _____

7. will not _____

8. does not _____

9. I will _____

10. they are _____

11. had not _____

12. there is _____

Connotation and Denotation ▪ For each underlined word, write (-) for a negative connotation, (+) for a positive connotation, or (N) for a neutral connotation.

_____ **1.** Jake told us a <u>story</u> at the party.

_____ **2.** Jake is such a <u>showoff</u>.

_____ **3.** He <u>brags</u> about his sense of humor.

_____ **4.** Often he tells a <u>hilarious</u> story.

_____ **5.** This story was <u>dull</u>.

_____ **6.** In fact, I got <u>bored</u>, so I left.

_____ **7.** I went home and fell <u>asleep</u>.

_____ **8.** I slept <u>peacefully</u> all night.

_____ **9.** Sue <u>giggled</u> at the joke.

_____ **10.** She <u>wept</u> at the last act.

_____ **11.** Suddenly he <u>snarled</u>.

_____ **12.** The <u>curtain</u> came down.

_____ **13.** We <u>plodded</u> home.

_____ **14.** We ate <u>delicious</u> muffins.

Idioms ▪ Underline the idiom in each sentence. Then write the meaning of the idiom on the line.

1. The band's new song didn't knock my socks off.

_____

2. I was out like a light the moment my head hit the pillow.

_____

3. He flew off the handle when he learned his car had been stolen.

_____

4. Her smile lit up the sky.

_____

5. Makoto let the cat out of the bag when he mentioned the surprise party.

_____

6. She was down in the dumps after she missed the speech.

_____

7. The good news from his sister put him on cloud nine.

_____

8. She was on the fence about the invitation.

_____

Types of Sentences ▪ Before each sentence, write **D** for declarative, **IN** for interrogative, **IM** for imperative, and **E** for exclamatory. Punctuate each sentence correctly.

1. _____ This dinner is delicious___

2. _____ Please pass the pepper___

3. _____ Where are the forks___

4. _____ I'm starving___

5. _____ What's in that bowl___

6. _____ Does anyone want more___

7. _____ Ouch, I burned my tongue___

8. _____ I'd like another roll___

9. _____ Eat more slowly___

10. _____ Who wants to clear the table___

Parts of a Sentence ▪ Underline the word or words in each sentence that are identified in parentheses.

1. (compound predicate)   Ellen typed and proofread her report.

2. (indirect object)   Matt, lend me your black pen.

3. (simple subject)   The report is excellent.

4. (direct object)   The instructor gave the report an "A."

5. (subordinate clause)   The first draft that Ellen wrote was 12 pages long.

6. (complete predicate)   She read her notes six times.

7. (complete subject)   Everyone in the class chose a different subject.

8. (simple predicate)   All the reports were completed in two weeks.

9. (independent clause)   The reports had to be in on time, or they would lose a grade.

10. (adverb clause)   I finished before the due date.

Parts of a Sentence ▪ Underline each subordinate clause. Then write **adjective** or **adverb** on the line.

_____ 1. The lawyer who defended the criminal was just doing her job.

_____ 2. The concert was over before we knew it.

_____ 3. It was the first time that Edward had been to Niagara Falls.

_____ 4. Although it was still early, Pamela left to go home.

_____ 5. Canada is a beautiful country that people like to visit.

_____ 6. When Rebecca heard that, she became very angry.

_____ 7. The horse kicked because it had never been saddled before.

_____ 8. Safety has become more important since the crime rate began to rise.

_____ 9. The people whose last names begin with "M" can enter now.

_____ 10. After the way Joe acted, I don't want to see him again.

Complex Sentences ▪ **To each group of words below, add a subordinate clause or an independent clause to create a complex sentence.**

1. Paul forgot the directions _____

2. After it was dark _____

3. This wasn't planned _____

4. When we took a couple of wrong turns _____

5. Before crossing the bridge _____

6. While looking for a map _____

7. When he asked for directions _____

8. No one had heard of the street _____

9. Three hours later _____

10. Before the trip home _____

Compound Sentences ▪ **Create compound sentences by adding an independent clause to each group of words.**

1. Walter bought a new hunting dog _____

2. She called to change her tickets _____

3. It was too late for Tom _____

4. We decided to stay at home _____

5. Leaders from several countries came _____

6. You can leave it there _____

7. It's possible that I am wrong _____

8. The wind picked up _____

Run-on Sentences ▪ **Correct each run-on sentence by writing it as two sentences or as a compound sentence.**

1. It was the middle of the night, the smoke alarm went off we woke up frightened.

_____

2. The reason we called you here is clear, we need to make some decisions today.

_____

Expanding Sentences ▪ **Expand the sentence by adding details to answer the questions What kind? and How many? Write the expanded sentence on the line.**

The butterflies migrated.

_____

Parts of Speech ▪ Write the part of speech above each underlined word. Use the abbreviations given in the box.

n.	noun
pron.	pronoun
v.	verb
adj.	adjective
adv.	adverb
prep.	preposition
conj.	conjunction

1. We had grilled steak, baked potatoes, and a fresh tossed salad for dinner.

2. The exhausted hikers quickly set up their tents and went to sleep.

3. The Japanese gardener pruned the young fruit trees and rose bushes carefully.

4. Anthony tried very hard to finish the mystery novel, but he fell asleep.

5. The island's tourists quietly watched the glorious sunset until it disappeared.

Verbs ▪ Underline the correct verb, and circle the verbal in each sentence.

1. Gardening (is, are) Mr. and Mrs. Butala's favorite hobby.

2. Dean (received, will receive) his swimming medal tomorrow.

3. We (driven, drove) to the lake to fish for trout.

4. The pitcher (has tried, have tried) to throw the runner out.

5. Roberto (chose, chosen) to wait in line for a ticket.

6. The thief (broken, broke) into the office to steal equipment.

7. Mary (have decided, has decided) to move to a new town.

8. The dried spices (smells, smell) wonderful.

Pronouns ▪ Underline the pronoun in parentheses that agrees with the antecedent in each sentence. Circle each antecedent.

1. Scott's brothers gave him (their, his) suggestions.

2. The children took care of the wounded bird and then set (them, it) free.

3. The coach was interviewed by reporters after (his, their) game.

Adjectives and Adverbs ▪ Complete each sentence with the proper form of the adjective or adverb in parentheses.

1. (early) We arrived at the party _____ than the other guests.

2. (expensive) The groceries for the cookout were _____ than the ones

   for the birthday party.

3. (tall) Is Luis the _____ player on the basketball team?

4. (fresh) Use this loaf of bread for the sandwiches since it is _____ than mine.

Grammar and Usage ▪ **Fill in the blanks by supplying the word or words specified in parentheses.**

Manatees _____ mammals whose population is endangered. Also
        (linking verb)

known as sea cows, manatees have dark gray skin, a very small head, poorly developed

eyes that _____ see _____, and two front
        (contraction of do)   (adverb)

flippers. _____ tails are large, rounded flippers. Manatees live
        (possessive pronoun)

_____ shallow, fresh water or saltwater and eat underwater plants.
        (preposition)

They _____ in the southeastern part _____
        (intransitive verb)   (preposition)

the United States, western Africa, South America, the Amazon, and the Caribbean Sea.

Manatees are _____ gentle animals. _____
            (adverb)   (gerund of rub)

muzzles is how they communicate. If alarmed, _____ make a
                                              (subject pronoun)

_____ noise. By adulthood, they grow to between eight and fifteen feet
(present participle of chirp)

_____ weigh _____ 1,500 pounds. Scientists
    (conjunction)   (adverb)

studying _____ adult manatee _____ observed
        (limiting adjective)   (helping verb)

that it can eat about 100 pounds of plants in one day.

Manatees _____ clean waterways by eating vegetation before it blocks
        (helping verb)

narrow passages. In some areas, manatees are encouraged _____,
                                                          (infinitive of thrive)

so they _____ waterways free of plants. Boats and boat propellers
        (future tense of keep)

are the _____ enemy of the manatee. In a few places, people hunt
        (superlative adjective)

_____ for meat, oil, and hides. _____
    (object pronoun)   (demonstrative adjective)

hunting has led to the decline of the manatee population. _____,
                                                           (conjunction)

in most areas, manatees _____ by law.
                        (protect in passive voice)

Capitalization and End Punctuation ▪ Circle each letter that should be capitalized. Write the capital letter above it. Add the correct end punctuation to each sentence.

1. our neighborhood holds a block party every june____

2. will the organizers be mrs. hernandez and dr. altman____

3. a local restaurant, charlie's place, is donating pizzas and italian sandwiches____

4. my street will be closed off on saturday and sunday from clark st. to prairie lane____

5. mr. johnson of the store bikes for you is judging the bicycle decorating contest____

6. will the country kitchen at oakland ave. donate 100 pies for the pie-eating contest____

7. last year's champion, mark gable of rosemont, says, "i'm ready for all

   the blueberry pies you can give me____"

8. dancers and singers from the phillips school will perform scenes from

   robert louis stevenson's *treasure island*____

9. the road race begins at the corner of maple and crane streets at 8:00 A.M. on saturday____

10. there are runners entered from carlyle, rosemont, meadow grove, and newton____

Using Other Punctuation ▪ Add commas, quotation marks, and apostrophes where needed in the sentences below.

1. Why are you telling me all this now asked Cynthia.

2. You can use books encyclopedias and atlases when doing research.

3. Ive spent the last two hours waiting said Mary.

4. Scott said Youll be much happier when you get settled.

5. Lloyd Jane and Debra are all going in the same car.

6. Wont you please help me with this asked Joe.

7. Shes the one said Ellen who brought that wonderful dessert.

8. Nissans Hondas and Toyotas are Japanese automobiles.

9. My fruit salad recipe she said calls for oranges apples bananas and raisins.

10. Karen mowed the yard weeded the garden and watered the flowers.

11. Saras car was in the shop for two weeks.

12. Janet Rosa and Alicia went to Dianes dinner party.

Apostrophes ■ **Insert apostrophes where they are needed in the sentences below.**

1. I cant find the consultants report anywhere.

2. The teams new uniforms werent sewn properly.

3. Doesnt that store sell womens jewelry?

4. The horses owner wouldnt sell them for any price.

5. Cant you pick up Stephanies car for her at the repair shop?

Colons and Hyphens ■ **Add colons and hyphens where they are needed in the sentences below.**

1. Our meeting is at 130 this afternoon, and you need to remind the fol
lowing people Jim Brown, Patricia West, Ann Tyler, and Jeff Ray.

2. My brother in law helped us move into our second story apartment.

3. Between 100 and 500 yesterday, twenty five people signed the sign up sheet for
the conference.

4. That well known Italian restaurant specializes in the following foods lasagna,
grilled shrimp, veal, and spaghetti with meatballs.

5. My great grandfather will be eighty seven years old tomorrow.

Punctuation and Capitalization ■ **Circle each letter that should be capitalized. Add commas, quotation marks, apostrophes, periods, hyphens, and colons where needed.**

1230 e. clark st.
san diego, ca 94024

mr. charles martinelli
3340 w. belden street
san diego, ca 94022

Dear mr. martinelli

on june 10 and 11, our neighborhood will be holding its fifth-anniversary summer block party____ it is a day-long event with contests performances great food and sidewalk sales____ in past years, local restaurants and businesses have donated food and prizes____ we hope your restaurant charlies place will join in and help make our block party a success____ i remember you once saying id love to pitch in next time____ please call us at 555 1270 and let us know if youll want to contribute this year____ we look forward to hearing from you soon____

Sincerely,
angela hernandez

Topic Sentences ■ **Write a topic sentence for the paragraphs below. Name a possible audience for each paragraph.**

1.   All children and adults should learn basic first aid. Courses are offered through schools and community groups. You never know when you'll need to clean a wound or use a more difficult technique during an emergency. By knowing first aid, you'll always be prepared.

Topic Sentence: _____

Audience: _____

2.   Butterflies and moths fly from flower to flower, looking for pollen. When they land on a flower, some of the sticky pollen rubs off on their legs. When they fly to another flower, it rubs off onto the new flower.

Topic Sentence: _____

Audience: _____

3.   Many people walk or run to stay healthy. Others swim or play sports for exercise. Some people prefer indoor exercises, such as using exercise videos and machines.

Topic Sentence: _____

Audience: _____

Supporting Details ■ **Underline the two sentences that contain details that support the topic sentence.**

1. **Topic Sentence:** A meteor looks like a bright streak of light in the sky.

   a. A meteor leaves a trail of hot gas.

   b. A meteor blazes across the sky as it travels through space.

   c. I saw a meteor fall from the sky.

2. **Topic Sentence:** Ants are called social insects.

   a. Ants live together in colonies and help each other.

   b. Ants are pests, and they can ruin a picnic.

   c. Ants share their food and their work.

3. **Topic Sentence:** Alligators and crocodiles are alike in many ways.

   a. Alligators have wider heads and shorter jaws than crocodiles.

   b. They are both reptiles and have rough skin.

   c. Alligators and crocodiles live in and near the water.

Revising and Proofreading ▪ Rewrite the paragraphs below. Correct the errors by following the proofreader's marks.

Proofreader's Marks

≡	⊙	ⓈⓅ
Capitalize.	Add a period.	Correct spelling.
/	∧	¶
Make a small letter.	Add something.	Indent for new paragraph.
∧	ℯ	→
Add a comma.	Take something out.	Move something.

¶ did you know that roughly three-quarters of the earth's fresh water is held not in rivers and lakes? the water is held in glaciers, lage sheets of ice that form in high altitudes and polar regions, such as antarctica and Greenland their are between 70,000 and 200,000 glaicers in the world.

¶ as temperatures warm, glaciers melt a little and move at a wrate that can't bee seen as they move, they sometimes freize and add to their mass before moving on they actually reshape the land they pass ovver. the most famus glaciers are in europe the best-known ones are in the french and swiss alps.

_____

_____

_____

_____

_____

_____

_____

_____

_____

_____

_____

Using the Dictionary ▪ Use the dictionary samples to answer the questions.

earn (ûrn) *v.* **1.** to receive in return for work done. **2.** To become deserving or worthy; *Nancy earned first place in the tournament.* [Middle English *ernen*, from Old English *earnian*]

earth (ûrth) *n.* **1.** The third planet from the sun. **2.** The dry land of the planet. **3.** Soft, loose, dirt suitable for planting. [Middle English *erthe*, from Old English *eorthe*, related to Old High German *erda*, earth, from Greek *eraze* to the ground]

1. Circle the letter of the guide words for the above entry.

   a. east / ebb   **b.** each / easily   **c.** each / eagle

2. How many definitions are listed for earn? _____ earth? _____

3. Write one sentence using the second definition of earth.

_____

4. Write the most commonly used definition of earn. _____

_____

5. What part of speech is earn? _____ earth? _____

6. How many syllables do earn and earth have? _____

7. Write the respelling of earn. _____ earth. _____

8. Which word came from the Old English word earnian? _____

9. Which word means the same in Old High German as it does in modern English? _____

Parts of a Book ▪ Write title page, copyright page, table of contents, or index to tell where you would find this information.

_____ 1. The page on which specific information can be found

_____ 2. The author's name

_____ 3. The page on which a chapter begins

_____ 4. The year the book was published

Reference Sources ▪ Write D for dictionary, E for encyclopedia, TH for thesaurus, AL for almanac, AT for atlas, or RG for *Readers' Guide* to tell where you would find this information.

_____ 1. an article on the Toronto Blue Jays

_____ 2. the etymology of the word baseball

_____ 3. the history of the Red Cross

_____ 4. the distance between Rome and Naples

_____ 5. a synonym for the word build

_____ 6. planning a vegetable garden

Using Visual Aids ▪ Use the map to answer the questions.

Poplar Point

1. What direction is the museum from the police station?

_____

2. How far is it from the museum to the recreation center?

_____

3. Does First Street run north/south or east/west?

_____

Using the Library and Card Catalog ▪ Use the sample catalog card to answer the questions.

Author Card

```
643.8
T 620

      Tambo, Frank L.
         Advances in computer technology–New York:
      Macmillan, 1993      271 p.
```

1. Who is the author? _____

2. What is the book's call number? _____

3. Who is the book's publisher? _____

Using a Thesaurus ▪ Use the sample thesaurus entry to answer the questions.

1. What is the entry word? _____

2. What part of speech is produce? _____

3. What are its synonyms? _____

produce *v. syn.* bear, yield, give, cause, make *ant.* waste, destroy

Using the *Readers' Guide* ▪ Use the *Readers' Guide* sample to answer the questions.

ICEBERGS
    Icehunters. [International Ice Patrol; cover story] M. Dane. il map
Popular Mechanics, 170:76–79 Oct '93

1. Who is the author of this article? _____

2. On what pages is the article? _____

3. Is the article illustrated? _____

Index

Abbreviations, 81
Accent marks, 108
Adjectives
  demonstrative, 66, 133
  limiting, 65, 133
  proper, 65, 80
  that compare, 67, 78, 133
  using, 65, 70, 102, 132–133
Adverbs
  that compare, 69
  using, 68, 70, 75, 79, 102,
   132–133
Almanac, 120, 121–123, 125, 138
Antecedents, 62, 77–78, 132
Antonyms, 1, 10, 12, 117, 128
Apostrophes, 6, 11, 39, 85,
  88–90, 134–135
Appositives, 40, 76, 78–79, 84,
  87
Atlas, 119, 121–123, 125, 138

Book, parts of, 111, 124, 138

Capitalization, 35, 65, 80–81,
  87–90, 134–135
Card catalog, 115, 124, 126, 139
Clauses, 25–28, 31–34, 63, 83,
  130–131
Clustering, 96, 102
Colons, 86, 88, 89, 135
Commas, 27, 40, 83–84, 87–90,
  134–135
Compound words, 7, 11, 86, 128
Conjunctions, 26, 27, 74, 76,
  78–79, 132, 133
Connotation/denotation, 8, 11,
  13, 129
Contractions, 6, 11, 85, 88–89,
  129, 133–135

Dictionary, 106–109, 110,
  121–126, 138
Direct objects, 23, 31–33, 53, 130
Double negatives, 75

Encyclopedia, 116, 121–123,
  125–127, 138
Etymology, 110, 124, 138
Exclamation points, 15, 31, 87,
  89, 130, 134–135

Gerunds, 55, 77, 132–133

Homographs, 3, 10, 12, 128
Homonyms, 2, 10, 12, 128

Hyphens, 7, 86, 88–90, 135

Idioms, 9, 11, 13, 129
Indirect objects, 24, 31–33, 130
Infinitives, 56, 77–78, 132–133

Library, using, 114–115, 124, 126,
  139

Nouns
  abstract, 36, 76, 79
  collective, 36, 76
  common, 35, 76, 132
  concrete, 36, 76, 79, 132
  plural, 37–38, 76, 132
  possessive, 39, 76, 85, 88, 132
  proper, 35, 76, 80, 88, 132
  singular, 37–38, 132
  using, 76, 79, 132

Outlining, 97, 103, 105

Paragraphs
  audience for, 95, 104–105,
   136
  ordering information in, 94
  supporting details in, 93, 96, 99,
   102, 104–105, 136
  topic/topic sentences in, 92, 95,
   96–99, 102, 104–105, 136
Participles, 57, 77, 132–133
Periods, 14, 15, 31, 82, 87–90,
  130, 134–135
Persuasive writing, 98–99,
  103–105
Predicates
  complete, 16–17, 31, 33, 130
  compound, 21, 31, 33, 130
  simple, 18, 31, 130
Prefixes, 4, 10, 13, 128
Prepositional phrases, 72–73,
  78–79, 102
Prepositions, 71, 76, 132–133
Pronouns
  antecedents for, 62, 77–78, 132
  demonstrative, 61
  indefinite, 61, 76, 78
  object, 60, 64, 77, 133
  personal, 60, 76
  possessive, 60, 76–77, 132–133
  relative, 26, 63, 78
  subject, 60, 64, 76–77, 132–133
  using, 60, 76, 132–133

Question marks, 15, 31, 82, 87,
  89, 130, 134

Quotation marks, 85, 87, 89,
  134–135
Quotations, 80, 83–84, 85, 87, 89,
  134–135

Readers' Guide, 118, 121–123,
  125, 127, 138–139
Reference sources, using,
  121–123, 125, 138
Revising/proofreading, 100–101,
  103, 105, 137

Semicolons, 27, 86
Sentences
  combining, 22, 32, 33
  complex, 27–28, 31–34, 130,
   131
  compound, 27–28, 31–33,
   83–84, 86, 131
  definition of, 14
  expanding, 30, 34, 91, 102,
   131
  run–on, 29, 34, 131
  types of, 15, 31, 33, 130
  word order in, 19, 32, 34
Subjects
  complete, 16–17, 31, 33, 130
  compound, 20, 31, 33
  position of, 19, 32, 34
  simple, 18, 31, 33, 130
Suffixes, 5, 10, 13, 128
Synonyms, 1, 10, 12, 117, 128

Thesaurus, 117, 121–123, 125,
  127, 138–139
Title, personal, 81

Usage
  lay/lie, 59
  may/can, 58
  sit/set, 59
  teach/learn, 58
  who/whom, 64

Verbs
  intransitive, 53, 78, 133
  mood of, 52, 79
  passive, 54, 79
  phrases, 42
  principal parts of, 41
  tenses, 43–51, 77, 132–133
  transitive, 53
  using, 45–51, 76–77, 132–133
  voice, 54, 133
Visual aids, 112–113, 125, 127,
  139

Writing process. *See* Paragraphs.